80 E 12.50

PUMP SELECTION

PUMP SELECTION
A Consulting Engineer's Manual

Rodger Walker, P.Eng.
Associated Engineering Services Ltd.
Vancouver, British Columbia, Canada

 **ann arbor science** PUBLISHERS INC.

POST OFFICE BOX 1425 • ANN ARBOR, MICHIGAN 48106

$T J$
900
$.W23$

First Printing, 1972
Second Printing, 1973
Third Printing, 1975
Fourth Printing, 1976
Fifth Printing, 1977
Sixth Printing, 1979

Copyright © 1972 by Ann Arbor Science Publishers, Inc.
P. O. Box 1425, Ann Arbor, Michigan 48106

Library of Congress Catalogue Card Number: 72-88891
International Standard Book Number: 0-250-40005-7

Manufactured in the United States of America

About the author—

Rodger Walker is a registered professional engineer in the Province of British Columbia, Canada. He joined Associated Engineering Services Ltd., Consulting Engineers, in 1957 and became an associate of the company in 1962. Mr. Walker, who specializes in the design of water treatment processes, pumping, and water supply systems for municipal, industrial, and oil field secondary recovery systems, has been responsible for a number of plant designs for the chemical and process industries in the United Kingdom, Canada, and the Middle East.

Contents

List of Tables

List of Figures

Foreword

In this age of sophisticated technology, it is difficult to appreciate the fact that, not too many years ago, the selection of pumping equipment for a water supply system was a major engineering decision.

In Western Canada in those early days, some of the most knowledgeable people were the pump suppliers and salesmen. Many of the smaller water supply systems were designed, constructed, and operated by people with very little technical and almost negligible practical knowledge of the subject. As a result, pump failures were frequent and many installations lacked efficiency and reliability.

The selection of the most suitable equipment for the job is still a decision of major importance. However, the situation has improved with the influx of more technical knowledge, most of it learned the hard way, through experience.

Associated Engineering Services Ltd., Consulting Engineers, has been involved in many projects requiring pumping equipment. The company's business has taken its engineers across the whole of Western Canada, including the Canadian Arctic and Subarctic—particularly to small towns and villages where the community was embarking on a water supply system for the first time.

AESL decided that, unless some guide lines for pump selection were published, this knowledge would be lost to the new graduate engineers as they entered the profession and some of the expertise would be lost to the industry. As a result, some of the now-senior engineers who were involved in the early "pioneer" days were asked to prepare talks on subjects which have now become their specialities.

These talks were presented at a series of in-house seminars where engineers and technicians were able to hear about some of the problems of the past and to discuss the developments of today. This interchange of knowledge and ideas is a most important and integral part of any con-

1

sulting engineering practice. Without it, the lessons of the past are soon
lost forever and have to be relearned the hard way.

A paper, "Pumps—from the Consulting Engineers View Point," was
prepared by Rodger Walker, P.Eng., for presentation at one of these
seminars. This was the means by which some of the knowledge acquired
by Mr. Walker came to be recorded and is now available as reference
material within the organization of Associated Engineering Services Ltd.

Now, through the medium of this publication, the information is presented for the guidance of others whose work involves them in decisions
relating to pumps and their application to industry.

Selection of Pumping Equipment

The procurement and installation of the most suitable pumping equipment from all the many available alternatives is a difficult proposition, made even more difficult by high pressure salesmanship from an overdeveloped industry. There are more than sixty manufacturing firms selling pumping equipment in the United States of America and Canada. Pump designers move extensively from company to company within the industry, with the result that the older brand names rarely retain any specific individualities of either design or workmanship. The larger, well-known companies are frequently less reliable and provide less after-sales service than the smaller and less-known companies.

The ultimate success of a pumping installation depends largely on the competency of the specification writer and the skill of the person who evaluates the quotations. The overall success of any installation is not necessarily the lowest initial cost but the lowest capital and operating cost over the economic life of the equipment, coupled with performance, reliability, and freedom from down time. Quotation evaluations should never be done in a hurry, and the final selection should not be made until complete documentation and terms of reference are on file. *Caveat emptor* (buyer beware) is particularly appropriate in this highly competitive business. Even with the best intentions on behalf of the manufacturer and his agent, the actual date of delivery is as unpredictable as the weather and is a vendor's promise to which it is almost impossible to attach any significance.

Owner's Philosophy

Moving liquids from one place to another, similar to mechanical handling, adds cost to the product but nothing to its value and should, therefore, be done as cheaply as possible.

As previously mentioned, the overall cost of pumping is not confined to the initial capital cost, but consists of

1. installed cost—amortization;
2. power or fuel costs;
3. supervision and maintenance; and
4. the cost of down time or standby equipment.

If we are to supply water to a municipality or pump sewage with a 100% reliability, standby units must be provided. Elevated water storage or sewage lift station wet well capacity may provide some buffer storage, but is usually sufficient for only a few hours. If the service is not critical and some down time can be accommodated, a less exotic pumping system may be justified, particularly if the increase in pumping costs can be written off with some tax relief.

The cost of borrowed money has an important bearing on the design of the most economical scheme. With rising inflation and higher labour costs, a pumping system designed for an economical life of twenty years or more will invariably be a better proposition if the operating cost can be kept to a minimum, even if this does mean a higher initial capital investment. If, on the other hand, borrowed capital is difficult to obtain and the economy appears to be in a tight anti-inflationary depression wherein labour costs are likely to be fairly stable, higher maintenance costs may be acceptable on a short-term basis. This approach is particularly true in the underdeveloped countries where there is an abundant amount of cheap labour, where the governments are anxious to increase employment, and where foreign capital is extremely difficult to obtain.

The Owner is responsible for the money he is authorized to spend. It is therefore important that the Owner's cash flow position is made known to the Engineer before the design is commenced. A convenient way of doing this is for the Engineer, after he has obtained his briefing, to prepare a concept report of his proposed scheme in sufficient detail to enable the Owner to understand the various implications involved and to advise the Engineer of the financing details. For example, there is not much logic in saving $20,000 or more in capital cost of a process industry at the expense of reliability if down time costs several thousand dollars per hour.

PUMP MANUFACTURER'S PHILOSOPHY

In order to remain in business, a pump manufacturer must sell equipment, and, since a pump is not regarded as a consumable item, a sale lost today is lost forever. On the other hand, a successful, conscientious pump supplier can usually look forward to a continuing business in spare parts and additional pumps when extensions to the plant are required.

Unfortunately, with our present economic system, we are frequently obliged to accept the lowest bidder. It is sometimes difficult, without specific adverse experience with a particular manufacturer's product, to justify a more expensive unit which will, in the Engineer's opinion, give a better performance pattern during its economic life. One of the ways in which the initial cost of a pumping unit, including the motor or engine drive, can be kept to a minimum is to use as high an impeller speed as possible, but the maintenance cost is increased considerably. Most pump and engine manufacturers have in the past built slow-speed units. Depending on their capacity, pumps would operate at motor synchronous speeds of 900, 1200, 1800 rpm, and with engine drives at even lower speeds. Unfortunately, one of the faults of the present economic system is that slow-speed pumps are no longer readily available, since their initial cost is higher and the competition for the lowest bid has forced them off the market. Some manufacturers have retained their old patterns and will still cast impellers and bowl assemblies as spare parts for existing pumps, but they are reluctant to market new pumps in the low-speed range. The reasons for this policy are that slow-speed pumps are not competitive compared to the higher speed pumps and that the frequency of spare-part replacement for slow-speed pumps is considerably less.

When the prices of spare impellers and bowl assemblies are compared to the initial cost of the pump, it becomes obvious that today's pump manufacturers must rely on the spare-part service for much of their business. It is the same old story of built-in obsolescence. If pumps lasted indefinitely, the majority of pump manufacturers would soon be out of business. We are frequently told that, with modern designs and with manufacturing techniques using new alloys and better materials, higher shaft speeds are perfectly satisfactory. These statements are valid only under ideal operating conditions, which are not normally encountered in municipal or industrial pumping installations. Once the machine is subjected to wear, corrosion, or erosion, the inevitable result is misalignment and vibration. The smooth, quiet-running pump becomes a veritable grinding machine accentuated by its higher rotative speed. The frequency of repairs quickly absorbs any savings in the initial cost. Unfortunately, the magnitude of these costs is rarely appreciated unless the Owner is aware of the problem and keeps accurate maintenance and operating costs against each item of equipment. One Canadian prairie town with a large number of well pumps to supply its water requirements found that it could buy new pumps from another manufacturer cheaper than it could service its existing units.

It is not the responsibility of the Engineer to try to change the entire economic climate—indeed, if he tried he would probably ruin it completely—but it is the Engineer's responsibility to understand the various situations as they develop, to advise his clientele accordingly, and get the best possible result from a poor set of circumstances.

CONSULTING ENGINEER'S PHILOSOPHY

A consulting Engineer's job is to study the problem and to devise the best scheme for achieving the required result. He must consider suction and discharge conditions, pressures and capacities, power and fuel supplies, detailed pump design, and, finally, capital and operating costs. It is possible that initially four or five schemes will evolve with apparently equal merit. It is then necessary to develop each scheme in greater detail in order to resolve into one or two viable schemes before going to tender.

During the preliminary investigations, discussions should take place between the Engineer and the pump suppliers to determine what equipment is available. Estimating prices will help considerably in determining the optimum scheme, but they are of only ball-park accuracy until the final invitations to tender are issued and the quotations are received.

The Engineer must give the pump suppliers as much data and general information as possible to ensure that the final quotations are representative of the best the industry has to offer. Typical examples of data sheets are included in the Appendices. Each supplier is asked to complete the data sheet and submit it with his quotation in order that all the submissions can be evaluated on equal terms. Unfortunately, some pump and engine suppliers are reluctant to do this, and will submit the quotations on only their own standard formats. In order to present a meaningful comparison, a tabulation sheet must be prepared by the Engineer, containing all the relevant data. It is obviously in the pump supplier's interest to present his case as completely as possible. If the Engineer has to search through the pump supplier's formal quotation to uncover the information he needs, there is a possibility that some of the data will be missing and the tabulation sheet will have a few blank spaces under that supplier's name and will be an incomplete submission. The general consulting Engineer is not usually a pump or engine designer. He will have some ideas as to what he is looking for in the pumps he proposes to use, but, on the other hand, he cannot be knowledgeable of all the new techniques available to pump manufacturers. The majority of pump suppliers will welcome a general outline of the Engineer's requirements in addition to the broad parameters of design which will include the following.

—Head
—Capacity
—Available Net Positive Suction Head (*NPSH*)
—Shaft speed preferred
—System head curve parameters
—Horse power characteristics
Whether or not there are any possibilities of the pumps operating at different discharge conditions than at the design point.
—Specific speed
Any particular limitations on specific speed with respect to cavitation should be stated.
—Suction conditions, including limits of submergence, suction head, or suction lift
—Drives, electric motor, or engine.

In addition to the numerical data, reference should be made to specific design codes where they are applicable.

—*American Standard for Vertical Turbine Pumps*[1]
—*Hydraulic Institute Standards*[2]
—"Centrifugal Fire Pumps"[3]
—Chapter 20, "Fire Pumps"[4]

Having provided the pump supplier with all the parameters within which he must comply, the specific details of the pump's design should be left to him and the completed questionnaire will inform the Engineer of the quality of the equipment that is being offered.

Efficiency of energy conversion is a prime consideration in municipal installations since power is often the largest item in the cost of operation. The annual power costs of each point of efficiency can be calculated and should be made known to the suppliers in the Invitations to Tender. Witnessing the pump tests and the receipt of the certified performance curves ensures the Engineer that the pumps are capable of the required performance, but it is of little value to purchase pumps on the basis of their good efficiency characteristics if they cannot be maintained in practice. The service facilities of the successful manufacturer and his agents are of considerable interest to the Owner. Equipment manufactured overseas must be adequately serviced by a large stock of spare parts carried in this country, since transportation strikes and labour disputes frequently disrupt overseas servicing arrangements.

NUMBER OF PUMPING UNITS REQUIRED

A three-pump system using identical electrically driven pumps each capable of supplying 50% of the maximum demand is a popular arrangement. The power supply only needs to be capable of operating two pumps at any one time. The economics of a four-pump system, each capable of 33⅓% of the maximum demand, should also be investigated.

If the power supply is subject to frequent failure and a continuous pumping operation is essential—for example, a fire pump station or a sewage lift station—then either engine-driven pumps or a standby diesel generator should be considered. If engine-driven pumps are the optimum choice, an additional unit should be installed to ensure continuity of performance. For example, a three-pump system in which each pump is capable of handling 50% of the load should be increased to a four-pump system on the basis that there will be two pumps in operation, one on standby, and one down for maintenance. If, on the other hand, a standby generator is preferred, reduced voltage starting will be required and the engine generator must be capable of supplying a starting current of at least three times the normal full load current. If sequence starting can be used whereby each pump can be started on the emergency supply in a stepwise manner, then a smaller emergency generator will suffice. Likewise, the generator necessary to supply emergency power to a four- or five-pump system could be smaller than the generator necessary for a three-pump system.

If the rate of water demand is variable and variable speed pumps are required, the use of wound rotor motors with Flomatcher controls has some advantages since the starting current for a wound rotor motor is equal to, or less than, the full load current. The engine-driven generator can be reduced to approximately a third of the capacity of the unit required to start squirrel cage induction motors of equal horsepower.

For small municipal installations, it is common practice to install pumps with dual drives. This scheme consists of an electric motor and also an engine connected through a common gear box to one pump. Unless floor space is of considerable importance, it is doubtful if this arrangement represents the best use of capital since the cost of the gear box and the clutches necessary to ensure that the two drives are independent is almost as much as another pump. One engine-driven plus one motor-driven pump is equivalent to twice the pumping capacity of the dual-drive unit and is a simpler system to control for very little extra capital cost.

In an endeavour to conserve power and to ensure that each pump is operating at its best efficiency, a "cascade system" consisting of three or more pumps of various capacities, but with the same total developed head and all capable of paralleling together, has frequently been installed. An automatic controller is provided to select the optimum combination of units to suit the water demand. Unfortunately, certain pumps in the series seem to operate for most of the time while the others are idle. For most installations, and particularly for smaller systems, it is better to have all the pumps of the same capacity. The system is more flexible to meet the water demands, maintenance is easier, and wear can be uniform; it is believed that these advantages outweigh any saving in power cost that may result from a cascade system. Larger installations, with high peak demands, may profit from a two-bank system whereby one bank of pumps will handle the normal demand and the second bank, in conjunction with first bank, will cope with the peak demands. It is possible that the second bank of pumps could be engine driven, and, in this way, peak power costs can be avoided.

To find the optimum number of pumping units requires a detailed study of power costs, system demand, maintenance, power outages, and environment. A diesel-engine–driven station may be the most economical to operate but would be unacceptable in a low-lying area surrounded by residential property or adjacent to a hospital.

Suction and Discharge Conditions

SUCTION CONDITIONS

More pumping installations fail because of poor suction conditions than from any other single cause. A centrifugal pump has no capability to "suck" from a lower level, such as a well, unless it is initially primed and all the air is removed. Whereas a reciprocating pump is capable of self priming, providing the plunger and valves are tight. A centrifugal pump is a kinetic energy machine designed to accelerate a volume of water from a low to a high velocity, and to convert this velocity into developed head at the pump discharge flange. The head developed depends upon the peripheral velocity of the impeller and is expressed as

$$H* \text{ (approximately)} = \frac{U^2}{2g}$$

where: H is total head at zero flow developed by the pump impeller in feet (same as shutoff head [SOH]).

U is velocity at the periphery of the impeller in feet per second.

g is acceleration due to gravity, 32.2 ft per sec^2.

Net Positive Suction Head (NPSH)

For a centrifugal pump to operate, the liquid must enter the eye of the impeller under pressure, usually atmospheric pressure, referred to as Net Positive Suction Head (*NPSH*). It is important to realize that there are two values of NPSH: the *available NPSH* which depends on the location and design of the intake system and can be calculated by the Engineer; and the *required NPSH,* determined by manufacturers bench scale

---

* This value in actual practice can be higher or lower than calculated by the formula, depending upon the type of impeller used.

11

tests. The required *NPSH* is the suction head required at the inlet of the impeller to ensure that the liquid will not boil under the reduced pressure conditions and the impeller will operate smoothly without cavitation. It is essential that the *available NPSH* exceeds the *required NPSH* with a reasonable margin of safety, at least two to three feet and more if possible. See Figure 1 and Figure 2.

Available NPSH

$$NPSH_{(available)} = H_{abso} + H_s - H_f - H_{vp}$$

where: $NPSH_{(available)}$ is Net Positive Suction Head measured in feet.

H_{abso} is the absolute pressure on the surface of the liquid in the suction well measured in feet.

H_s is the static elevation of the liquid above the centreline of the pump (on vertical turbine pumps to the entrance eye of the first stage impeller) expressed in feet. If the liquid level is below the pump centre line, H_s is a minus quantity.

H_f is the friction head and entrance losses in the suction piping expressed in feet.

H_{vp} is the absolute vapour pressure of fluid at the pumping temperature expressed in feet of fluid.

A "standard atmosphere" at sea level is equivalent to

1 atmosphere = 14.7 psi

= 760 mm mercury

= 29.92 in. of mercury

= 33.93 ft of water

With changes in altitude the "standard atmosphere" is modified.

Storms will also cause the atmospheric pressure to drop and 26 in. mercury (29.5 ft water) at sea level during a storm is not uncommon. This is equivalent to only 87% of the standard atmosphere (for practical purposes, assume 85%).

The vapour pressure of water increases with temperature which also reduces the available pressure at the pump suction.

EXAMPLE

A 3000 USgpm vertical turbine pump is located 4000 ft above sea level and is pumping water at a maximum temperature of 90°F. The suction bell is 24 in. in diameter, reducing to 12 in. in diameter at the first bowl assembly. The water level is never less than 8 ft above the first stage impeller. What is the available *NPSH* under the worst conditions?

TABLE 1. *Atmospheric Pressure at Various Altitudes*[5]

Altitude in Feet	Barometer Reading		Atmospheric Pressure	
	in. Hg	mm Hg	psia	ft of water
−1000	31.0	788	15.2	35.2
sea level	29.9	760	14.7	33.9
+1000	28.9	734	14.2	32.8
2000	27.8	706	13.7	31.5
3000	26.8	681	13.2	30.4
4000	25.8	655	12.7	29.2
5000	24.9	633	12.2	28.2
6000	24.0	610	11.8	27.2
7000	23.1	587	11.3	26.2
8000	22.2	564	10.9	25.2
9000	21.4	544	10.5	24.3
10000	20.6	523	10.1	23.4

TABLE 2. *Properties of Water*[5] [9]

Temperature °F	Absolute Vapour Pressure		Specific Weight lb/cu ft	Specific Gravity*	Absolute Viscosity (Centipoises)
	psia	ft of water			
32	0.088	0.20	62.42	1.0016	1.79
40	0.122	0.28	62.43	1.0018	1.54
50	0.178	0.41	62.41	1.0015	1.31
60	0.256	0.59	62.37	1.0008	1.12
70	0.363	0.89	62.30	0.9998	0.98
80	0.507	1.2	62.22	0.9984	0.86
90	0.698	1.6	62.12	0.9968	0.81
100	0.949	2.2	62.00	0.9949	0.77
110	1.275	3.0	61.86	0.9927	0.62
120	1.693	3.9	61.71	0.9903	0.56
130	2.223	5.0	61.56	0.9878	0.51
140	2.889	6.8	61.38	0.9850	0.47
150	3.718	8.8	61.20	0.9821	0.43
160	4.741	11.2	61.01	0.9790	0.40
170	5.993	14.2	60.79	0.9755	0.37
180	7.511	17.8	60.57	0.9720	0.35
190	9.340	22.3	60.35	0.9684	0.32
200	11.526	27.6	60.13	0.9649	0.31
210	14.123	33.9	59.88	0.9609	0.29

* Refers to water at 68°F, weighing 62.318 lb/cu ft, and having specific gravity of 1.000.

$$NPSH_{(available)} = H_{abso} + H_s - H_f - H_{vp}$$

where: H_{abso} at 4000 ft elevation is 29.2 ft.

under storm conditions (29.2×0.85) is 24.8 ft.

H_s is 8.0 ft.

H_f for a suction bell $\left[0.1\left(\dfrac{V^2}{2g}\right) \right]$ is 0.115 ft.

H_{vp} at 90°F is 1.6 ft.

Therefore:

$$NPSH_{(available)} = 24.8 + 8.0 - 0.115 - 1.6$$
$$= 31.1 \text{ ft}$$

For this installation, the required *NPSH* of the selected pump should not exceed 28 ft. It should be noted that the required *NPSH* increases as the capacity of the pump increases beyond the normal operating range (see Figure 3).

Cavitation

Cavitation is defined as the formation of cavities beneath the back surface of an impeller vane and the liquid normally in contact with it.

It can be caused in a centrifugal pump—

1. By the impeller vane travelling faster, at higher rpm, than the liquid can keep up with it.
2. By a restricted suction. (Hence, never throttle the suction of a centrifugal pump.)
3. When the *required NPSH* is equal to or greater than the *available NPSH*.
4. When the specific speed is too high for optimum design parameters.
5. When the temperature of the liquid is too high for the suction conditions.

The cavity consists of a partial vacuum, gradually being filled with vapour as the liquid at the interface boils at the reduced pressure in the cavity. As the cavity moves along the underside of the vane towards the outer circumference of the impeller, the pressure in the surrounding liquid increases and the cavity collapses against the impeller vane with considerable force. A pump which is cavitating can usually be detected by the noise inside the casing, but this is not always the case. When a pump impeller is examined, the evidence that cavitation has occurred will be deep pitting and general erosion on the underside of the vanes some distance from the impeller inlet. If a pump is cavitating due to a temporary upset in the system, the cavitation can sometimes be reduced by allowing a small amount of air to enter the pump suction or by throttling the pump discharge valve. These are temporary expedients and are used only until the problem can be finally eliminated.

Intakes

In most states, provinces, and territories of the North American continent, permission must be obtained from the appropriate authorities before an intake can be installed in a river or lake. Not only are the health authorities concerned, but also the departments responsible for navigable watercourses. In some cases, the procedures are complex, particularly if the waterway is extensively used for navigation. Special protection of the intake structures are often necessary to minimize the possibilities of damage from ships' keels and anchors. Whenever a plant design is contemplated, an early approach to the governing authorities will frequently save many frustrations and much wasted effort.

Intake Sump

Intake sump designs have changed considerably during recent years. Reference should be made to *Hydraulic Institute Standards.*[2]

Complicated baffled walled designs are no longer favoured since they tend to cause vortexing. However, it is important to ensure that one side of the suction bell is almost touching one wall of the pump chamber and that the bottom opening is reasonably close to the floor in accordance with the recommendations of the Hydraulic Institute. Additional side clearance is necessary for vertical turbine pumps, particularly if they have a deep setting and small diameter columns, since the lower extremities of the pump column will gyrate. If this movement is restricted by rubbing against the wall, bearing problems may develop. See Figure 4.

Protective Screens

Protective screens should always be provided whenever there is possibility of suspended or floating debris entering the pump suction. A ball of discarded electrician's insulation tape or a roll of plastic foil can be particularly damaging to the bowl assembly of a multistage vertical turbine. However, wire screens bolted or welded directly on to the suction bowl as protection devices are not recommended. They can cause serious suction problems if they become plugged, and there is always the possibility that they may corrode, fail, and be drawn into the pump suction, causing the damage they were designed to prevent.

Fish Screens

Fish screens are also mandatory in many states and provinces to protect the juvenile salmon and trout. Specific requirements relating to the watercourse must be obtained from the appropriate government departments. Stationary screens with clear openings of 0.1-in. or less are frequently required, with approach velocities not exceeding 0.1 ft per second. However, in certain cases velocities of 0.4 ft per second are acceptable, depending on the location of the intake and the fish population. Self-cleaning mechanical screens are frequently used wherever there is a possibility of continual obstruction from debris.

A level differential cell should be installed with sensing elements on either side of the screens to measure the head loss and to provide an alarm when abnormal differential head conditions occur due to plugged screens. A low-level cut-out switch should also be installed on the pump side of the screen to stop the pumps when there is insufficient water in the pump wet well to provide adequate *available NPSH*.

DISCHARGE CONDITIONS

The total discharge head of a pumping installation consists of a static head or static lift and a friction head or dynamic head.

Static Head

The static head is measured from the surface of the liquid in the suction well to the surface of the liquid at the discharge reservoir. (See Figure 5.) Variations in terminal levels both at the suction well and at the discharge reservoir must be considered when calculating the upper and lower limits of the static head.

Friction Head

This is the head lost in overcoming pipe friction and depends on the size of pipe, smoothness of the inside surface, the number and type of fittings, orifice plates and control valves, velocity of flow, and viscosity and density of the liquid. The most up-to-date correlation of these factors is expressed in the Colebrook equation.

$$\frac{1}{\sqrt{f}} = -2 \log \left(\frac{k}{3.7D} + \frac{2.51}{Re \sqrt{f}} \right)$$

where: f is friction coefficient $2gDi/V^2$
k is a linear measure of effective roughness
D is pipe diameter
Re is Reynolds number $(DV)/v$
V is velocity in feet per second
v is kinematic viscosity of the fluid
g is gravitational constant (32.2)
i is hydraulic gradient

This equation is too cumbersome and contains too many variables to be of practical use in the above format, however, the Institution of Water Engineers in their *Manual of British Water Engineering Practice*[6] has published a nomograph (see Figure 6) entitled "Universal Pipe Friction Diagram" based on the work of Prandtl, Von Karman, Nikuradse, and Colebrook. This nomograph is sufficiently accurate for most practical purposes and is superior to the Hazen-Williams equation. Greater accuracy can be achieved with the use of this nomograph if the velocity (V) is pre-calculated and plugged into the nomograph together with the internal pipe diameter (D) instead of using (Q) (quantity: thousands of imperial gallons per hour) and the pipe diameter (D), which has too short a "length of sight" for accurate alignment. (See Appendix 4 for velocity tables.)

The roughness coefficient K expressed in inches is a measure of the actual roughness of the pipe surface. Recommended roughness values of K in inches are given in Table 3.

Total Head

The total head developed by the pump can be expressed by one of the following equations (see Figure 5):

PUMP WITH SUCTION LIFT
$$H = h_d + h_s + f_d + f_s + (V^2/2g)$$

PUMP WITH SUCTION HEAD
$$H = h_d - h_s + f_d + f_s + (V^2/2g)$$

where: H is total head in feet of liquid pumped when operating at the desired capacity.

h_d is static discharge head in feet, equal to the vertical distance between the pump datum and the surface of liquid in the discharge reservoir. (The datum is taken from the shaft centre line of horizontal centrifugal pumps or the entrance eye of the first stage impeller of vertical turbine pumps.)

h_s is static suction head or lift in feet equal to the vertical distance from the water surface to the pump datum. (Notice that this value is positive when operating with a suction lift and negative when operating with a suction head.)

TABLE 3.   *Recommended Roughness Values*[7]

	Values of "K" in inches		
Pipe Materials	Good	Normal	Poor
Class 1			
Smooth materials—drawn copper, aluminum, brass, plastic, glass, fiberglass		0.0005	
Class 2			
Asbestos cement		0.001	
Class 3			
Bitumen lined cast iron		0.0015	
Cement mortar lined steel		0.0015	
Uncoated steel	0.001	0.0015	0.003
Galvanized iron	0.003	0.008	0.015
Uncoated cast iron	0.007	0.015	0.030
Class 4			
Old tuberculated water mains, with the following degrees of attack:			
Slight	0.025	0.06	0.15
Moderate	0.06	0.15	0.25
Severe	0.60	1.5	2.5
Class 5			
Woodstave pipe	0.015	0.030	0.060
Class 6			
Smooth surface precast concrete pipe in lengths over 6 feet with spigot and socket joints internally pointed.	0.003	0.006	0.015
Precast pipes with mortar squeeze at the joints		0.15	0.30
Class 7			
Gravity sewer pipes (new)	0.030	0.060	0.15
Gravity sewer pipes (dirty)	0.25	0.50	1.0

f_d is friction head loss in the discharge piping measured in feet.

f_s is friction head loss in the suction piping measured in feet.

$(V^2/2g)$ is velocity head in feet. For vertical turbine and submersible pumps, the velocity head is measured at the discharge flange. However, for booster pumps and centrifugal pumps, as shown in Figure 5, the velocity head developed by the pump is the difference between the $V^2/2g$ at the discharge flange and the $V^2/2g$ at the suction flange. That is,

$$V^2/2g = (V^2d/2g) - (V^2s/2g)$$

where $V^2d/2g$ is velocity head at the discharge flange.

$V^2s/2g$ is velocity head at the suction flange.

Since the discharge flange is usually a size smaller than the suction flange, the difference in the velocity head is always positive. Usually, it is a small percentage of the total head and is frequently erroneously neglected.

System Head Curve

The total discharge head for a municipal water supply is known as a system head curve and is plotted for various conditions of flow. A typical system head curve with two pumps operating in parallel is shown in Figure 7. In this instance, the system head curve is very flat, since only a very small portion of the total head is due to friction, and the two pumps in parallel will deliver almost double the flow of a single pump.

If, however, the system head curve is steep due to high friction losses (see Figure 8), the second pump operating in parallel with the first pump will deliver considerably less than double the original flow. The friction head loss in a pipe system is approximately proportional to the velocity squared, i.e., if the velocity is doubled, the head loss will be approximately four times the original value. This is illustrated in Figure 8, where one pump will deliver 4400 USgpm against a system head of 320 ft. If, however, two pumps are in parallel they will deliver 6500 USgpm (48% increase) against a system head of 700 ft and will absorb approximately 1440 hp compared to 446 hp for one pump only. This represents a 50% increase in flow for over three times the horse power.

Pipe Diameter

The economical or optimum pipe diameter can be determined graphically as illustrated in Figure 9.

OPTIMUM PIPE LINE DIAMETER

Where:

pipeline costs   = annual amortization cost of a unit length
                   of installed line (usually 1000 ft).

pumping costs = the annual power cost for a unit length
                 of installed line (1000 ft). (See Figure
                 10.*)

total cost   = summation of the pipeline cost and the
                   pumping cost.

The optimum pipe diameter is the one that has the least total cost, (in Figure 9, it is 18 in.). If the power cost increases, a larger pipe diameter would be more economical, and if pipe prices increase, a smaller pipe would be better.

It should be noted that the economical pipe diameter is selected on the basis of friction losses only and is not influenced by static head.

Having selected the optimum pipe diameter, the system head curve should be plotted—head against flow. The static head is the system head curve datum at zero flow. If the suction well level is subjected to seasonal variations which will affect the system head curve, a parallel curve should be shown for the system head curve under each set of conditions. Likewise, if the pumps are to discharge into an elevated tank, with upper and lower level limitations, this too should be indicated on the system head curve to ensure that all conditions of pump service are presented.

Pump Discharge Head

The pump discharge head can be specified in different ways, depending on the particular design code.

The *American Standard for Vertical Turbine Pumps*[1] defines "pump total head (H) as the bowl assembly head." This does not include the column and discharge head losses, which can be determined from graphs published in the *American Standard*.

With horizontal centrifugal pumps, it is usual to define the *Total dynamic head (TDH)*, as "the difference between the elevation corresponding to the pressure at the discharge flange of the pump and the elevation corresponding to the vacuum or pressure at the suction flange of the pump, corrected to the same datum plane, plus the velocity head at the discharge

---

* Figure 10 shows typical power costs in specific areas of British Columbia and is
  included in this book only to illustrate a convenient format for presenting the
  usually complicated schedule of costs.

flange of the pump, minus the velocity head at the suction flange of the pump."[9]

As previously mentioned, the head developed by a centrifugal pump impeller at shutoff head (*SOH*) is expressed thus:

$$H \text{ (approximately)} = U^2/2g$$

where: H = total head at zero flow, developed by each pump impeller in ft of liquid.
U = velocity at the periphery of the impeller in ft per sec.
g = acceleration due to gravity 32.2 ft per sec².

For multistage pumps, the total head is equal to:

$$\text{Total head (approximately)} = H \times \text{number of stages}$$

In Figure 11, all three identical pumps on the left of the diagram are operating with the same size impellers and at the same shaft speed. Notice that the heads developed by the pumps are independent of the weight of the liquid and the discharge head in feet is the same whether the pumps are handling brine with a specific gravity (SG) of 1.2, water at SG = 1.0, or gasoline at SG = 0.7.

The pressure gauge reading would be in accordance with

$$\text{psi} = \frac{\text{head in feet} \times \text{SG}}{2.31}$$

If, however, all three pumps are delivering liquids at 50 psi, as shown on the right of Figure 11, because of the difference in specific gravity of the liquids, each pump develops a different head. Therefore, if the speed of all three pumps is the same, the pump handling gasoline would have the largest diameter impeller and the pump handling brine would have the smallest.

Specifications

The developed head of a centrifugal pump is proportional to the peripheral speed of the impeller. A specific developed head can be obtained either by installing a larger diameter impeller and operating it at a lower speed or by installing a smaller diameter impeller and operating it at higher speeds, so that the circumferential velocity in both cases is the same.

The smaller impeller is housed in a smaller casing or bowl assembly and can therefore be built at a lower initial capital cost than the larger, slower unit. The faster the shaft revolves, the greater the wear in the bearings, wear rings, neck bushings, sleeves, and stuffing boxes. It is reported that the rate of wear and, therefore, the maintenance costs are proportional to the shaft speed squared, so that doubling the speed may result in four times the wear. Vibration becomes more pronounced as the wear increases the running clearances, and, since vibrations occur at greater frequency with higher shaft speeds, maintenance costs are higher than those of lower speed machines. If pumps are to be purchased on the basis of the lowest bidder, higher speed pumps will invariably be the result since they are less expensive to build (but more expensive to maintain).

Ball and roller bearings are commonly used on pumps and electric motors. They are relatively inexpensive but have a limited life which is highly dependent upon the degree of skill exercised in their initial installation. Their principal advantages are low cost and antifriction properties, since the rolling contacts between the stationary and rotating elements produce very little friction. They are, however, somewhat sensitive to damage by shock loads, changes in speed, ingress of foreign matter, and

23

poor lubrication. The pinpoint or knife edge contacts are very highly stressed under load and can readily be damaged, resulting in increased wear and shaft vibration. Wherever longevity, high rotational speeds in excess of 1800 rpm, and large horsepowers are required, oil-lubricated sleeve bearings and Kingsbury thrusts are preferred. Worn bearings result in vibration and, wherever possible, the shaft displacement should be measured and the bearings replaced if the following tolerances are exceeded. [9]

    900 rpm shaft displacement, peak to peak = 0.0050 in.
    1200 rpm shaft displacement, peak to peak = 0.0042 in.
    1800 rpm shaft displacement, peak to peak = 0.0035 in.
    3600 rpm shaft displacement, peak to peak = 0.0020 in.

The shaft tolerances should be measured at the top bearing of vertical turbine pumps and on the bearing housing(s) of horizontal pumps.

The most troublesome maintenance item of a centrifugal pump is the gland: whether a soft-packed stuffing box or a mechanical seal, it will give far less trouble if it operates at a lower shaft speed.

This is obviously an optimum balance between lower capital and higher maintenance costs as opposed to higher capital and lower maintenance costs. No doubt the balance is influenced by the current taxation laws; however, with increasing inflation, maintenance costs are rising sharply and therefore must be considered when selecting high speed pumping equipment.

Specific Speed (N_s)

The various implications and aspects of this parameter are dealt with in detail in published texts. [2, 9, 10] Specific speed is a correlation of pump capacity, head, and speed, and is a number expressed as follows:

$$\text{Specific speed } (N_s) = \frac{\text{rpm } \sqrt{\text{USgpm}}}{H^{0.75}}$$

where: rpm is shaft speed in revolutions per minute.
        H is head per stage in feet.

Specific speed places an upper limit on the shaft speed for any particular combination of total head, flow, and suction conditions. Impeller form and proportions vary with specific speed as shown in Figure 12. For double suction impellers, the total flow through the pump should be divided by two in calculating the specific speed; i.e., they should be considered to be two single-suction impellers operating in parallel.

The specific speed parameter (N_s) has many uses for the pump designer. For the pump applications engineer, it serves as a useful limitation in the design of suction condition. If a pump installation is within the specific speed limitations of the Hydraulic Institute,[2] the engineer can be reasonably certain that there will be fewer problems due to poor suction conditions.[9] Reference to the charts published in the *Hydraulic Institute Standards*[2] for the upper limits of specific speed (N_s) for any given type of impeller, first stage total head developed and suction lift or suction head conditions, will dictate the upper allowable shaft speed to comply with their recommendations. This upper limit should not be exceeded.

Suction Specific Speed (S)

Specific speed (N_s) is an index number indicative of pump type, whereas the parameter known as suction specific speed (S) is essentially an index number descriptive of the suction characteristics of a given impeller. It is defined as:

$$S = \frac{\text{rpm } \sqrt{\text{USgpm}}}{NPSH^{0.75}}$$

where: rpm is shaft speed in revolutions per minute
       NPSH is the *required NPSH* for satisfactory operation in feet

Note that, for double suction impellers, the flow in USgpm should be taken as one-half the total flow.

The upper limits of specific speed (N_s) and suction specific speed (S) are given in Figure 54–57 of the *Hydraulic Institute Standards*.[2]

WR^2

The expression WR^2 is used for defining the moment of inertia of a symmetrical body about a given axis, i.e., pump impellers, shafts, and rotors of electric motors. Actually, the moment of inertia is defined as $(WR^2)/g$, but is usually reduced to WR^2, where W is weight of the rotating body (in pounds); R is radius of gyration or the distance from the centre of rotation to a point at which the whole mass of the body is considered to be concentrated (in feet); and g is 32.2.

The WR^2 of a pump impeller is determined experimentally by the pump manufacturers and is given for water or other liquid. This parameter of pump design is used to calculate the required starting torque of the motor and to ensure that it is capable of accelerating the rotating mass up to synchronous speed without stalling.

Variable Speeds

Variable speed drives are becoming increasingly popular. Pump characteristics influenced by shaft speed are flow (gpm) varies directly with (rpm); head (ft) varies as the $(rpm)^2$; and horsepower (bhp) varies as the $(rpm)^3$.

To be able to reduce the rpm is analogous to having an impeller of variable diameter.

Initially, the only variable speed drives available were engines, steam and water turbines, or wound rotor motors. Later, induction motors with electromagnetic drives became available and, in the last few years, solid state variable speed controls for standard squirrel cage induction motors have been developed. The later devices are limited in their range and reduce the full load speed by approximately 20%. However, in most cases, 20% is all that is required to reduce the speed of a pump motor, since the developed head is proportional to speed squared. A reduction in rpm of 20% would result in a 36% reduction in head, which is usually all that is required to reduce the developed head to below the system head curve, with the result that the pump capacity, in relation to the system head curve, is reduced to zero.

The wound rotor motor, however, still has a place, particularly where engine-drive generators are installed to provide power to operate the pumps during periods of failure of the normal power supply. The starting current of a standard induction motor can be up to six times the normal full load current. Even with low inrush current motors and reduced voltage starting, the starting current may be as much as three times the normal full load current. However, a wound rotor motor can be started at reduced speeds below full load current; consequently, the capacity of the engine driven generator can be reduced to a nominal full load capacity machine, eliminating the necessity to purchase additional horsepower for the sole purpose of providing starting current.

Affinity Laws

The relationships between flow (gpm), head (ft), horsepower (bhp), and shaft speed (rpm), defined under the heading "Variable Speeds," are referred to as the "affinity laws" and are shown graphically in Figure 13.

PERFORMANCE CURVES

A typical performance curve for a vertical turbine pump is shown in Figure 3. The characteristic shapes of the curves for centrifugal, vertical turbine, and axial-flow pumps are shown in Figure 12.

It is important to select pumps with characteristic curves to suit the specific application. For example, if two centrifugal pumps are required to operate together in parallel, it is important that the head capacity curve has a uniform downward slope, as shown for the vertical turbine pumps in Figure 12. If, however, the curve is humped in the middle, as shown for the centrifugal pump, two pumps will not operate smoothly in parallel at this point on the curve, since there are two capacity values for the same head and they will continually "hunt" from one horsepower condition to another. It is also important to notice that the horsepower characteristics of a radial-vane impeller continue to increase as the head is reduced. With this type of impeller, the "run-out horsepower" will exceed the normal operating horsepower, and the motors, unless they are oversized for normal duty, will trip out on overload at low discharge heads. The vertical turbine impellers, also known as Francis-Screw impellers, have head-capacity (H-Q) curves with uniform downward slopes. They are able to run together smoothly in parallel without surging. Their horsepower reaches a peak near to the point of maximum efficiency and then slopes downward at reduced heads with the result that the motors operate at lower horsepowers as the flow increases. Axial flow impellers have their point of maximum efficiency at lower heads and have higher capacities than the other two impeller types. These pumps are frequently used on low head irrigation schemes.

When selecting the most suitable pump from a number of supplier quotations, it is advisable to plot all the curves on the same scale. Figure 14 shows three typical H-Q curves from three different manufacturers. All three pumps are in accordance with the *Standards of the National Fire Protection Association.*[3] Curve A has preferred characteristics to B or C, since it has a lower shut-off head and generally better performance characteristics to the right of the rated point of 231 ft at 1500 USgpm. This pump was selected and, when it was factory tested, the curve shown as AA in Figure 14 was the actual certified performance curve.

It must be emphasized that published characteristic performance curves are at the best only good approximations, and a manufacturer will guarantee only one or two points on the H-Q curve generally in the range of maximum efficiency.

It is almost impossible to test a pump on site in complete accordance with the requirements of the *Hydraulic Institute Standards*,[2] and any tests below the requirements of this standard are not generally regarded as acceptable. Therefore, the only way in which the owner can be certain that he is getting the performance he specified is to witness the factory test and make certain that the pumps are tested in accordance with the requirements of the Hydraulic Institute and are capable of producing the performance characteristics quoted in the specifications. If the witnessed factory tests do not come up to the standards anticipated, it is usually possible to polish the impellers or the diffuser vanes in the casing, until the required results are obtained. If the published characteristics cannot be obtained by modifications to the impeller or casings, the manufacturer should reimburse the owner accordingly. If it is inconvenient for the owner or his representative to witness the test, the owner should insist on a signed certified performance curve giving the necessary data obtained under test bed conditions.

Efficiency

The efficiency of a large installation can be a critical factor when choosing the optimum pumping units from a number of competitive quotations. This can be illustrated by the following example.

A municipal pumping station is to house three vertical turbine pumps, each capable of pumping 3000 USgpm against a 200-ft head. Three pumps will operate together in parallel for 50% of the year, and two pumps in parallel for the remaining time. The average power cost for the whole station can be taken at approximately one cent per kilowatt hour. Calculate the monetary value of one percentage point of efficiency.

From a brief look at a number of catalogues, it would appear that most manufacturers have pumps capable of this performance at efficiencies ranging from 83% to 87%. Using 85% as an efficiency datum:

$$\text{Horsepower (hp)} = \frac{3000 \times 8.35 \times 200}{33,000 \times 0.85}$$
$$= 178.5$$

Efficiency of a 200 hp induction motor will be approximately 92% plus a further 2% for transformer and switchgear losses, so that the overall electrical efficiency will be approximately 90%.

$$\text{Kilowatts per pumping unit} = \frac{178.5 \times 0.746}{0.9}$$
$$= 148 \text{ kw}$$

Total kilowatt hours per year (365 days = 8760 hours)

Three pumps in operation for 50% of the time:
$3 \times 8760 \times 0.50 \times 148 = 1.94 \times 10^6$ kwh

Two pumps in operation for 50% of the time:
$2 \times 8760 \times 0.50 \times 148 = 1.295 \times 10^6$ kwh

Total power consumption:
$(1.94 \times 10^6) + (1.295 \times 10^6) = 3.235 \times 10^6$ kwh per year

Annual power costs at one cent per kwh = $32,350 per year

From a similar calculation, but using a pump efficiency of 84% instead of 85%, the annual power cost would amount to $32,800, an increase of $450 per year which is approximately equivalent to a capital expenditure now of $4500 based on an interest rate of 8% for 20 years (present worth value). This sum divided by three is equivalent to $1500 per pump per one percentage point of efficiency.

The comparative values of five competitive quotations are tabulated as follows:

Quotation Number	Basic Unit Price (dollars)	Pump Efficiency (percent)	Bonus or Penalty (dollars)	Comparative Price (dollars)
1	18,500	85	. . .	18,500
2	17,200	84	+1,500	18,700
3	19,000	86	−1,500	17,500
4	16,500	83½	+2,250	18,750
5	20,000	87	−3,000	17,000

On the basis of comparative price, Quotation 5 is the "best buy." Provided the pumps are to be tested in accordance with the *Hydraulic Institute Standards*[2] and competently witnessed, there should be no difficulty in ensuring that the pumps are capable of their specified test bed performance. However, the question as to whether or not they will continue to operate at the specified efficiency with the minimum of maintenance depends on shaft speed, pump design, workmanship, materials of construction, column diameter, lubrication, bearings, and other features. Therefore, it is essential to ensure that, if a premium price has been paid for a high efficiency pump, the efficiency can be maintained at its peak performance throughout its economic life. Otherwise, it would be better to recommend Quotation 3 or even Quotation 1. It should be noted that, in the example shown, the lowest basic unit price has the highest comparative price, assuming that, apart from power costs, all other annual operating costs are equal for the five quotations.

STUFFING BOXES

The stuffing box requires more attention during the operating life of a pump than any other single item, and a small defect can prevent the pump from performing satisfactorily. The function of the stuffing box and gland is to provide a liquid-tight seal between a rotating element (shaft) and a nonrotating element (casing). The packing consists of a soft semiplastic material which is cut in rings and fits snugly around the shaft or shaft sleeve. There is usually a slotted metal lantern ring approximately halfway down the stuffing box to permit leakage of fluid through the inner rings to provide lubrication and to reduce pressure on the outer rings of packing. Alternately, where gritty liquids are handled, clean water under pressure is forced into the stuffing box through the lantern ring to keep the abrasive grit from getting between the packing and the shaft.

Stuffing boxes always need to be lubricated, either internally by allowing water to pass up through the packing and leak to atmosphere or by forcing water, oil, or grease to the packing through the lantern ring and, at the same time, allowing a small external leakage. A gland must never be tightened to the extent that there is no leakage; otherwise the packing will quickly overheat, shrink, and fail. Excessive leakage will result in having to unpack the stuffing box and remove all the old packing. To facilitate repacking the stuffing box, it is important to ensure that the manufacturer has provided adequate clearances. In some cases, it is possible to remove the gland and use the casing pressure to push out the old packing; this greatly simplifies the task of removing the old packing. It is essential to ensure that all the old packing has been removed and there are no broken pieces jammed in between the bottom neck bushing and the shaft, since old packing can be severely abrasive to the pump shaft or sleeve.

When starting a new pump for the first time, the gland nuts should be loosened to allow an adequate leakage of water to lubricate the packings. The nuts should be tightened only by an experienced pump mechanic when the pump is running. Never tighten the gland nuts when the shaft is stopped. If the stuffing box leakage cannot be controlled to a reasonable rate after completely repacking, the problem may be due to loose or worn bearings, misalignment, or an out-of-balance impeller. If the pump has been in service for some time, the problem may be due to a worn shaft or sleeve. In spite of their obvious disadvantages, stuffing boxes are still preferred for certain installations. Pumps approved for fire protection service by the Canadian Underwriters Association are all fitted with stuffing boxes rather than mechanical seals.

Pumps installed in isolated pump stations are often fitted with packed stuffing boxes since they rarely fail completely without warning.

In many instances, however, mechanical seals have been used to considerable advantage over the old packed stuffing boxes, and, in the pumping of certain nonlubricating fluids, only mechanical seals can be used.

MECHANICAL SEALS

Mechanical seals are available in many different designs and with many features, and the choice of the most suitable seal for a particular pump on a specific service is one for the specialist. The right mechanical seal in the right application can be an excellent investment and will frequently give trouble-free operation for many years. Most pumps can be supplied with either a stuffing box or a mechanical seal, and the choice as to which to install is usually left to the engineer. If the pump is to handle water or sewage, either system of sealing the shaft against leakage is applicable. Seals are more expensive in initial cost, but, provided the pump bearings are good and the rotating parts are well balanced and maintained, the maintenance cost of the seal will be negligible. If, however, the pumps will be handling gritty fluids and the bearings are likely to become worn with little or no preventative maintenance, then stuffing boxes are preferred. Never install mechanical seals on an old pump in the belief that they will be less troublesome than the original stuffing boxes unless the pumps have been completely overhauled with new bearings, the shaft reground if necessary, and rotating parts balanced and completely realigned. In one pumping installation, a new vertical turbine pump with a 75hp motor operating at 1800rpm, fitted with a mechanical seal valued at over \$1000, failed after three days' operation. A new seal was fitted and this also failed after running for a few days. It was eventually discovered that the third line-shaft bearing down the pump column had excessive clearance. When this fault was corrected, the pump and seal worked well together for many years. Usually, when a mechanical seal fails, it is due to excessive vibration or malalignment of the pump shaft, rather than an actual seal failure. However, when a seal does fail, there is a considerable amount of high pressure leakage and care must be taken to ensure that no vulnerable items of electrical equipment are in the line of fire. It is always advisable to have splash guards fitted around mechanical seals and stuffing boxes to prevent severe leakages from causing undue damage.

When deciding whether or not to use mechanical seals, it is advisable to ask the pump supplier for his recommendations and to request two alternative prices: pump complete with mechanical seal; and pump complete with stuffing box.

As a further check, it is advisable to ask the mechanical seal manufacturer for his recommendation for the specific installation. Also make certain that a competent representative of the mechanical seal manufacturer is in the area. A broken mechanical seal may result in a pump being out of service for days or even weeks, whereas a stuffing box can usually be repacked within a few hours. If the pumps are likely to be well maintained and run under good operating conditions, it is possible that the mechanical seal will be worth the extra cost. However, if good maintenance and operating conditions cannot be ensured or if a mechanical seal failure could remain unnoticed for several days, it is possible that a soft packed stuffing box would be preferred.

NONREVERSE RATCHETS

Wherever possible, centrifugal pumps are started and stopped against closed or partly closed discharge valves. However, if a pump stops due to power failure and the discharge valve or check valve does not completely close, there is the possibility that water will pass through the pump contrary to the normal direction of flow and will rotate it in the reverse direction. The net head at the pump impeller is usually less than the static head at the pump discharge because of friction in the discharge head and pump column. The reverse rotational speed is a function of the specific speed (N). Higher specific speeds result in higher rates of backspin. The actual rate of backspin under specific operating conditions can usually be obtained on request from the pump manufacturer. Usually, however, the reverse speed of an actual installation is approximately the same as the normal forward speed, and is invariably below the maximum safe rotational speed of the pump components. There is no danger of unscrewing the pump shafts, although they are rotating in the direction opposite to normal, because they are being driven from the opposite end of the shaft by a pump impeller operating as a water turbine rather than by the electric motor. There is, however, a very decided danger to the motor and pump if power is restored to the motor when it is rotating in the reverse direction. To avoid this problem, nonreverse ratchets have frequently been installed in the upper housings of vertical electric motors. They have been quite satisfactory in relatively small horsepower units. However, in larger horsepower units, the nonreverse ratchets have not only been unreliable in an emergency but have disintegrated the upper housing of the motor. They should, therefore, be specified with extreme caution and for small horsepower units only, and a manufacturer's guarantee that they will function without failure should be obtained.

To prevent a motor from being inadvertently energized when it is in the process of backspinning, a rotational switch should be installed on the top housing of the motor to effectively lock out the starter whenever the pump is backspinning.

MATERIALS OF CONSTRUCTION

Pump manufacturers are usually well up to date in the use of materials for pump construction. Provided the engineer factually describes, with as much data as possible, the fluids to be pumped, the manufacturer will furnish a pump constructed from the most suitable materials. Engineers' requests for quotations frequently ask for materials specifications (see Appendix 1, Typical Pump Data Sheets). Reference should also be made to the appropriate section in the *Hydraulic Institute Standards*.[2] This data is of considerable value in assessing the properties of various materials of pump construction if a maintenance inspection indicates that components are showing abnormal signs of wear due to corrosion or erosion. The defective components can then be replaced with parts made from more suitable materials.

Stainless steel is frequently used in pump construction with excellent results, but it should be used with caution. With anaerobic sludges devoid of free oxygen, certain stainless steels are attacked. Two stainless steels rubbing together can cause serious abrasion problems to the machined surfaces. Two adjacent aluminum components suffer from the same problem. As a general rule, the surface hardness of two adjacent rubbing components should be separated by at least 50Bhn on the Brinell hardness number scale. One component could be case hardened or sprayed with molten metals of different surface properties. In this way, the structural strength of the material is retained and optimum surface characteristics are obtained.

VALVES AND PIPING

A centrifugal pump should be started with a closed or restricted discharge valve. At shut-off head and zero flow there is no danger of cavitation when the pump is operating under stable conditions with minimum horsepower and presumably adequate net positive suction head. A vertical turbine pump at shut-off head has maximum downthrust. However, once stable conditions have been established, the pump must not be permitted to continue to operate under shut-off head conditions for more than a few seconds, since heat equivalent to the horsepower input at shut-off head will be generated in the bowl assembly or casing. Figure 3 shows that the brake horsepower at shut-off head (SOH) is 575 bhp. One horsepower is thermally equivalent to 42.4 Btu per minute, so that the heat generated in the bowl assembly will be 24,400 Btu per minute. Assuming that the heat capacity of the bowl assembly, filled with water, is equivalent to approximately 500 lb of water, the temperature rise at SOH will be approximately 50°F per minute. There would be some cooling from the water in the wet well surrounding the bowl assembly; however, it would not be long before the water in the bowls would be boiling and the water in the column would be displaced by the steam. The shaft bearings and stuffing box or mechanical seal would run dry, resulting in considerable damage.

It is sometimes expedient to operate a pump for short periods at shut-off head, but there must be sufficient circulation of fluid through the pump impellers to remove the heat generated by the horsepower absorbed. An arbitrary rule for calculating the required flow is

$$\text{Flow (USgpm)} = \frac{\text{horsepower at shut-off head}}{4}$$

For the vertical turbine pump in Figure 3, the flow of 144 USgpm would result in a temperature rise of 20°F. Even this may be too high a temperature rise for a deep-well vertical turbine pump if there is any likelihood of differential expansion between the pump shaft and the casing which may result in reducing the impeller clearances.

Surge Control Valves

For relatively small pumping applications, it is customary to install a surge control valve between the pump discharge flange and the check valve. (See Figure 15, Surge Control Valve.) The valve is fully open when the pump is started and passes sufficient flow in the fully open position to prevent the developed head from reaching the system head curve requirements. (See Figure 16, Surge Control Valve Setting.) In this case, two pumps are designed to operate in parallel against a rising system head curve. The surge control valve should be designed to pass 4000 USgpm at 100-ft head (or 43.3 psi). The pump will be operating in the stable operating range, although at the opposite end from the shut-off head position. Providing the suction conditions are correctly designed and the pump is operating within the limits of the required *NPSH,* there should be no danger of cavitation. As soon as the pump is running at full speed, the surge control valve slowly closes and the developed head increases until it reaches the point of intersection with the system head curve. In this way, the pump goes on line with the minimum of surge and water hammer. Likewise, the surge control valve must be slowly opened prior to stopping the pump. The time to close the surge control valve when the pump is starting and the time to open the valve when the pump is stopping must exceed the time required for the reflection of the shock wave, equal to $2L/a$ seconds, where L is the length of pipe in ft; and a is the velocity of the shock wave, usually 4000 to 4500 ft per sec.

When a vertical turbine pump is stopped, the water in the column will tend to drop to the level in the wet well. This will occur if air can enter the pump through the surge control valve or if the water level is below 30 ft (see Table 1). If the water level in the well is deeper than approximately 30 ft below the ground surface, the water level in the column will fall until it can be supported by the prevailing atmospheric pressure. If it is a deep well where the level of the aquifer is 100 ft or more below the pump discharge head, there will be a partial vacuum in the top 70 ft of column, assuming that the stuffing box or mechanical seal is bottle tight and the check valve does not leak. When the pump starts, it momentarily discharges against zero head until it has pumped sufficient water to fill the column. Under these conditions, the pump will be operating off the head capacity curve at the extreme right-hand end, with the result that the motor may stop on overload before sufficient head has been developed to reach stable pumping conditions. This is frequently a fault with the installation of deep-well submersible pumps.

If a partial vacuum exists in the top section of a pump column, a considerable pressure surge can develop when the pump starts and the water in the column hits the underneath side of the pump discharge head. The pressures resulting from these shock waves exist for only fractions of a second, but they have been known to crack the pump discharge head castings. Allowing air to enter the column through a surge control valve does tend to cushion the shock wave and assists in building up the developed head, thus reducing the problems associated with starting pumps against zero head conditions. The air admitted to the pump column is discharged to atmosphere through the surge control valve, but it is important to ensure that the surge control valve is open long enough for all the air to escape before it closes and the pump discharges to the system. The venting of air can be noisy, particularly with large high head pumps.

Hydraulic Surge Suppressors

Pumps are frequently operated to maintain a municipal water supply system within prescribed limits of pressure. For example, a pump station consisting of two or more pumps may be required to maintain a certain level of water in an elevated reservoir several miles away from the pump station. The distribution system will probably be connected to the main between the pump station and the elevated storage. This is a fairly common arrangement and has the advantage that a fire can be supplied with water from both the reservoir and the pump station at the same time. The pumps are usually operated to maintain a prescribed water level in the elevated storage tank by sensing the pressure in the pump discharge header at the pump station. The pressures in the pump header are influenced by demand changes in the distribution system, and the pumps are frequently started and stopped in response to surge pressures rather than level changes in the elevated tank. To reduce these fluctuations at the pressure switch in the pump station, a surge suppressor can be located between the main and the pressure switch. (See Figure 17, Hydraulic Surge Suppressor.) This will usually reduce the frequency and amplitudes of the surges sufficiently to sense the level changes in the elevated tank. If, however, the distribution system is operating close to its upper limit of capacity, the surges may be too much for a simple hydraulic suppressor and control by a float switch and signal cables may be the only answer to this problem.

DRIVES

Electric Motors

The majority of pumps are driven by squirrel cage induction motors. Synchronous motors are also used for larger horsepowers, particularly if power factor correction is important. Wound rotor motors are occasionally used for variable-speed drives. Electric motors are relatively trouble-free and, with their associated transformers and switchgear, are almost as reliable as the power supply. Reduced voltage starting and low inrush current motors are frequently used for the higher horsepowers where a momentary reduction in line voltage at starting would adversely affect other consumers. In the selection of low inrush current motors with reduced voltage starters, it is important to ensure that the starting torque developed by the motor as it runs up to speed is in excess of the torque requirements of the pump; otherwise a stalemate condition will occur, the unit will fail to get up to speed, and the starter will trip out on overload. Water-cooled motors are also available; they are quieter than air-cooled machines and offer many advantages in the larger horsepowers where air conditioning of the building would be required to absorb the heat from the motors.

Thrusts

The axial thrusts of vertical turbine pumps are usually absorbed by the motor bearings, and care must be taken to ensure that they are adequate to absorb the loads involved. A pump is always operating at the extreme right end of the head capacity curve under conditions of zero head, at the instant it starts to rotate. The water enters the pump through the bell mouth in an upward direction and is deflected radially outward by the pump impeller. This change in direction of flow results in an upthrust which lifts the pump shaft. If the pump is located in a deep well or connected to a vertical solid shaft motor there is probably enough weight in the shaft and the rotor of the motor to counterbalance the upward thrust. As soon as the pump develops head, the upthrust diminishes and a downthrust develops.

The magnitude of the downthrust is a function of discharge head and impeller areas, and is at a maximum at shut-off head. If the downthrusts are excessive, Kingsbury thrust bearings are preferred. They consist of a number of babbitt metal tilting thrust pads which transmit the load from the shaft thrust collar to the pump discharge head or motor casing. The whole thrust assembly is enclosed and runs in oil similar to a plain babbitt metalled bearing. In the selection of a pump driver, whether it be an electric motor or a right-angle gear drive from an engine, it is essential to ensure that the thrust bearings have adequate capacity to absorb the thrusts involved and a reasonable anticipated life under these conditions.

Operating Costs

The cost structure varies considerably between the different power companies and from one state or province to another. In some areas, there is a maximum demand charge which can adversely affect the use of standby equipment or the use of additional pumps to meet peak demands. Before deciding on electric motors for large pumping installations, the use of diesel or gas engines should also be investigated.

Engines

The possible use of engines as opposed to electric motors may be ruled out on the basis of noise, vibration, space, maintenance, and required operating attendance. If, however, the power supply is unreliable or expensive and the environment problems are not insurmountable, the use of engines should be considered. The maintenance cost of various types and makes of engines is sometimes difficult to obtain. Speed and horsepower ratings of engines are extremely critical with regard to maintenance. If a pumping unit is to operate on a continuous basis, it is advisable to select an industrial-type engine operating at 600 to 900 rpm and install a gear box to increase the shaft speed to suit the pump requirements. If, however, the pumping unit is only required to operate during peak demand periods or during a power failure, then higher speed units can be used. The breakeven point between high capital cost and low maintenance costs (slow-speed units) as compared to low capital cost and high maintenance costs (higher speed units) can be determined only after a detailed cost evaluation for each specific application has been made. Gas turbines have also to be considered in these installations. It is understood that the maintenance cost and down time of an industrial gas turbine is appreciably less than piston engines of equivalent horsepower.

If an engine-driven pump is required to start immediately the electric pumps stop due to power failure, then it is advisable to consider a diesel rather than a gasoline or natural gas engine. The capital cost of the diesel engine is usually higher than the gas or gasoline engines, but they are easier to start and therefore more reliable. The gas engine, unless it is used frequently, will often require extensive cranking due to the gummy deposits on the pressure-regulating valves. Likewise, the gasoline engines always seem to have too rich or too weak a mixture and require considerable persuasion before they will start. On the other hand, a well-maintained and well-adjusted diesel engine will usually start on the first crank. A further advantage is that a diesel engine will take full load almost immediately it is up to operating speed, whereas a gasoline engine usually does not operate well until it reaches its normal operating temperature.

Comparison of Fuel Costs

Fuel costs vary from location to location, and each application must be evaluated on its own merits. Table 4 provides data from which fuel cost in terms of cents per brake horsepower hour (ϕ/bhp-hr) can be calculated.

Dual Fuel Engines

A dual fuel engine is basically a compression ignition diesel engine capable of aspirating a weak mixture of natural or sewage gas and air, compressing it, and igniting the mixture with an injection of diesel oil. The engine can operate equally effectively as a straight diesel engine using liquid fuels only or as a dual fuel engine using 95% to 96% gas and 4% to 5% fuel oil. The above ratios are based on the calorific values of the two fuel components. The compression ratio of the dual fuel engine is the same as a diesel engine, between 14:1 and 16:1.

TABLE 4. *Comparison of Engine Fuels*

Fuel	Heating Value	Specific Gravity	Typical Engine Fuel Consumption
Natural gas	980–1160 Btu/cu ft	0.61 (air = 1.0)	11,000 Btu/bhp-hr) (approx. 11 cu ft/bhp-hr)
Diesel fuel	168,000 Btu/imp gal	0.82–0.95 (water = 1.0)	8900 Btu/bhp-hr (0.47 lb/bhp-hr)
Propane	110,000 Btu/imp gal	0.51 (liquid) (water = 1.0)	11,000 Btu/bhp-hr (0.51 lb/bhp-hr)
Gasoline	150,000 Btu/imp gal	0.70–0.78 (water = 1.0)	11,200 Btu/bhp-hr (0.56 lb/bhp-hr)

Natural and sewage digester gases are high in methane content. With weak gas-to-air ratios, methane-air mixtures can be compressed in the cylinders of a dual fuel engine without detonation. At the end of the compression stroke, diesel oil is injected into the cylinders and immediately ignites and burns the gas-air mixture. The efficiency of the dual fuel engine is said to be 0.5% to 1% better than a straight gas engine, due to the superior ignition qualities of compression ignition as compared to spark ignition. Dual fuel engines are commercially available from 250 bhp to over 6000 bhp. Their capital cost is higher than for a straight diesel engine, but they have several important advantages. They can be started and put on load using liquid fuels in exactly the same manner as a normal diesel engine. They can run on cheaper, cleaner, gaseous fuel at considerably less cost than a straight diesel engine. Advantage can be taken of the cheaper gas rates for an interruptable gas supply service, since the engine can revert to 100% diesel fuel immediately the gas supply fails. This transition from 95% gaseous and 5% oil to 100% fuel oil can be automatically accomplished with only a momentary fluctuation in speed. As soon as the gas supply is restored, the engine can switch back to using a gaseous fuel-oil mixture. It is understood that maintenance costs are appreciably less for a dual fuel engine compared to spark ignition engines.

Exhaust Heat Recovery

The heat supplied to an engine is utilized and dissipated as follows:

Heat to useful work	30% approx.
Jacket cooling	30% approx.
Exhaust heat	30% approx.
Loss to radiation and oil cooling	10% approx.

If there is a convenient use for low-grade heat, a jacket and exhaust heat-recovery system can be employed with advantage. Engines always work more efficiently and with less maintenance if the jacket cooling water temperatures are uniformly high at all conditions of load. One method of achieving this is with the use of a vapour-phase heat-recovery system where the jacket water temperature is kept above 260°F in a pressurized system. Exhaust gases are cooled in a water-cooled silencer with a total net recovery from jacket cooling and exhaust gases of up to 50% of the heat supplied to the engine. Steam can be generated up to 25 psi. If higher pressures and temperatures are required, the engine heat recovery system can be used to preheat feed water to a boiler. A further advantage in the use of water-cooled exhaust gas heat-recovery systems is the reduction in noise. If low-grade heat can be economically used for space heaters, low pressure process steam, or hot water, there may be a good case for using engines as opposed to electric motors.

Maintenance

An end suction or split case centrifugal pump casing can easily be distorted by excessive pipe stresses imposed by the pipe system during installation. Before starting a new pump, it is advisable to slack off the gland nuts and endeavour to turn the shaft by hand. If it is a large pump, a bar or a socket wrench may be required to obtain adequate leverage. If it is too stiff to turn, it may be advisable to uncouple the suction and discharge pipe flanges to determine if there is any spring in the pipes. In many cases, several inches of spring may result, particularly if the pipe-fitter started at the pump flanges with the piping installation; by the time a few lengths of pipe are installed, several thousand pounds of stress may be locked up in the system, resulting in severe strain on the pump casing. This is particularly true if there are appreciable changes in temperature between installation and normal operation.

It is also advisable to check the holding-down bolts with a torque wrench to ensure they are evenly tightened. If the shaft is still too stiff to turn by hand, the coupling bolts should be removed and the two halves of the coupling separated and checked for axial alignment. The same routine should be repeated after a few months of operation to ensure that there has been no movement between the pump and its driver which could result in malalignment.

A pump unit which has operated satisfactorily for a number of years may suddenly start to develop gland and stuffing box troubles or bearing failures. An alignment check will frequently reveal the true source of these problems. Pumping units and piping systems are never completely static, but there is always some movement due to expansion or shrinkage which must be corrected if trouble-free operation is to be achieved. Meth-

41

ods of checking alignment and other pump maintenance techniques are described in the *Hydraulic Institute Standards.*[2]

RECORDS

There should always be a card or a data sheet available in the plant office for each item of equipment installed or available in the stores. The data should include all salient information concerning the pump and motor. See Appendix 2, Typical Maintenance Data Sheet and Maintenance Record.

It is the duty of the plant superintendent to ensure that history sheets are kept up to date and all down time, emergency repairs, and routine maintenance are recorded. The cost of parts and their availability are of vital importance to the economic operation of the installation. Information of this nature is invaluable when considering obsolescence and whether it is more economical to repair or to replace.

References

1   *American Standard for Vertical Turbine Pumps,* Ref. ASA B58.1–
    1961 (AWWA E101–61). Published by American Water Works
    Association Inc., 2 Park Avenue, New York, N.Y. 10016.
2   *Hydraulic Institute Standards for Centrifugal, Rotary & Reciprocat-
    ing Pumps,* 12th edition, 1969. Published by the Hydraulic Insti-
    tute, 122 East 42nd Street, New York, N.Y. 10017.
3   "Centrifugal Fire Pumps," CUA 20. *Standards of the National Fire
    Protection Association.* Published by Canadian Underwriters' As-
    sociation, Fire Protection Engineering Division, 460 St. John Street,
    Montreal, P.Q.
4   Chapter 20, "Fire Pumps." Reprinted from the *Handbook of Indus-
    trial Loss Prevention.* Published by McGraw-Hill, and copyright
    1967 by the Factory Mutual Engineering Corporation.
5   *Hydraulic Handbook,* 5th edition. Published by Colt Industries,
    Fairbanks Morse Pump and Electric Division, 3601 Kansas Avenue,
    Kansas City, Kansas 66110.
6   *Manual of British Water Engineering Practice,* 4th edition, 1969.
    Edited by William Oswald Skeat, published for the Institution of
    Water Engineers, London, England, by W. Heffner & Sons Ltd.,
    Cambridge, England.
7   Ackers, P. *Tables for the Hydraulic Design of Storm-drains, Sewers
    and Pipe-lines,* Ministry of Technology, Hydraulics Research Sta-
    tion; Hydraulics Research Paper No. 4. Published by HMSO
    (1963). (NOTE: Values in Table 3 have been recalculated from
    the above tables and modified as necessary to conform with North
    American practice.)
8   *Glossary Water and Waste Water Control Engineering,* 1969. Pub-
    lished jointly by the APHA, ASCE, AWWA, WPCF.
9   Gartmann, H. *DeLaval Engineering Handbook,* 3rd edition, 1970,
    McGraw-Hill.
10 Karassik, I., and Carter, R. *Centrifugal Pump, Selection, Operation
    and Maintenance,* 1960, McGraw-Hill.

APPENDIX 1

Figures

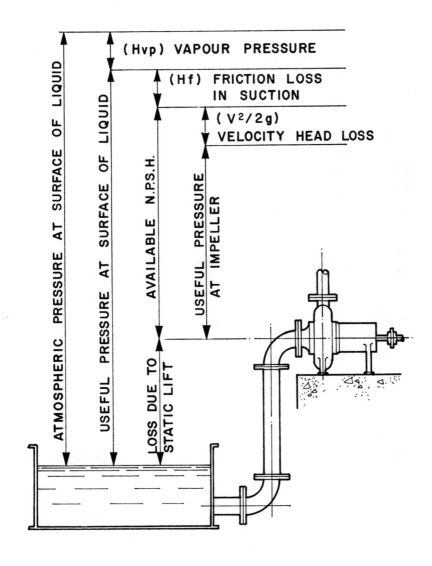

FIGURE 1. *NPSH centrifugal pump with lift.*

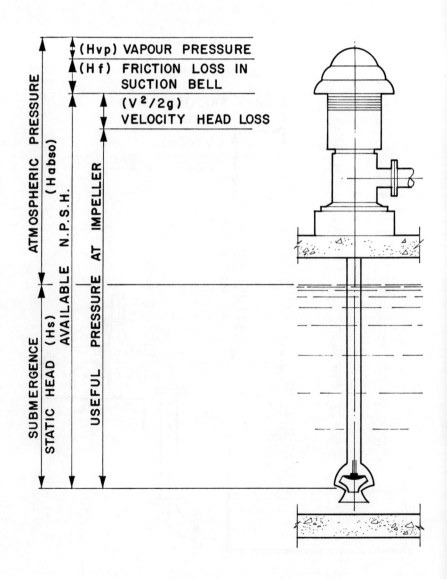

FIGURE 2. *NPSH vertical turbine pump.*

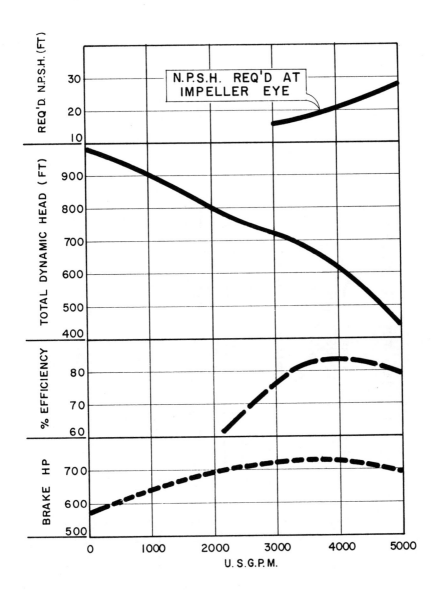

FIGURE 3. *Typical vertical turbine characteristic curves.*

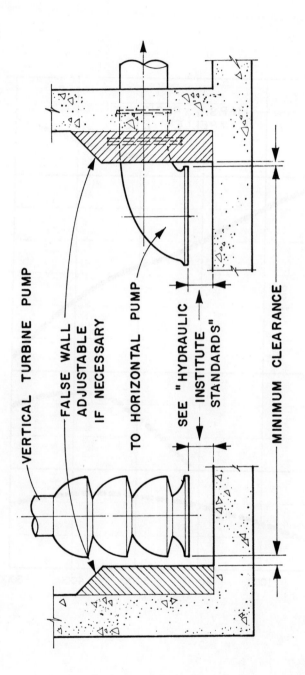

Figure 4.   *Pump inlet design.*

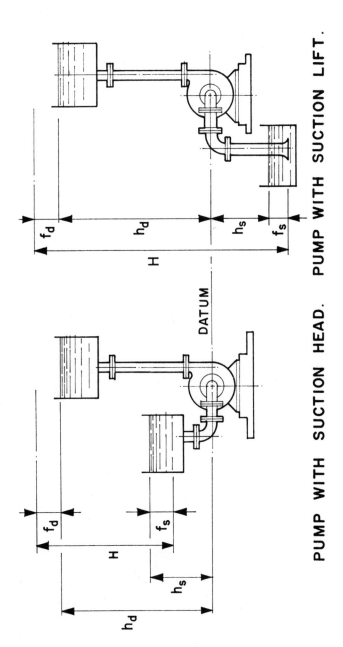

PUMP WITH SUCTION HEAD.   PUMP WITH SUCTION LIFT.

FIGURE 5.   *Pump heads.*

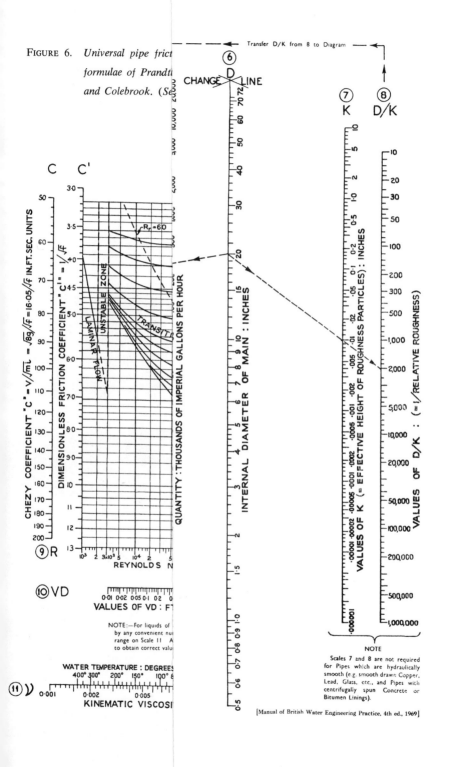

FIGURE 6. *Universal pipe friction* *formulae of Prandtl* *and Colebrook. (Se*

Transfer D/K from 8 to Diagram

⑥ CHANGE D LINE

⑦ K   ⑧ D/K

NOTE

Scales 7 and 8 are not required for Pipes which are hydraulically smooth (e.g. smooth drawn Copper, Lead, Glass, etc., and Pipes with centrifugally spun Concrete or Bitumen Linings).

NOTE:—For liquids of by any convenient nu range on Scale 11 A to obtain correct valu

⑨ R   REYNOLDS N

⑩ VD   VALUES OF VD : FT 0·01 0·02 0·05 0·1 0·2 0

⑪ ν   WATER TEMPERATURE : DEGREES 400° 300° 200° 150° 100° 6 KINEMATIC VISCOSI 0·001 0·002 0·005

CHEZY COEFFICIENT "C" = V/√mL = √8g/√F = 16·05/√F IN.FT.SEC. UNITS

DIMENSIONLESS FRICTION COEFFICIENT "C'" = 1/√F

QUANTITY : THOUSANDS OF IMPERIAL GALLONS PER HOUR

INTERNAL DIAMETER OF MAIN : INCHES

VALUES OF K (= EFFECTIVE HEIGHT OF ROUGHNESS PARTICLES) : INCHES

VALUES OF D/K : (= 1/RELATIVE ROUGHNESS)

[Manual of British Water Engineering Practice, 4th ed., 1969]

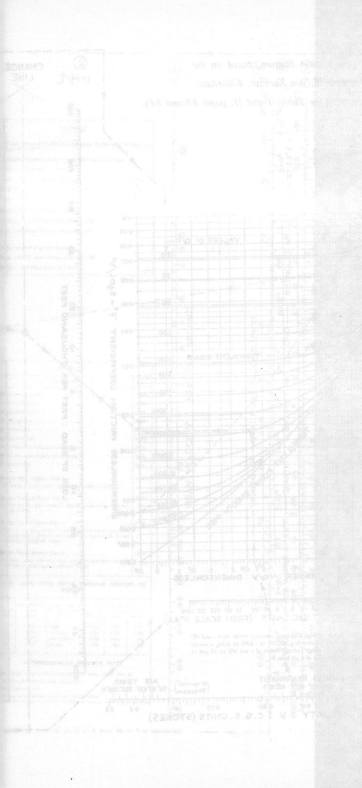

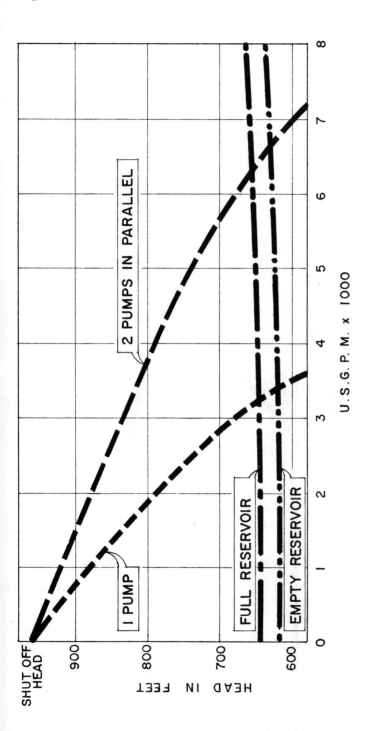

FIGURE 7.　*System head curve with low friction loss.*

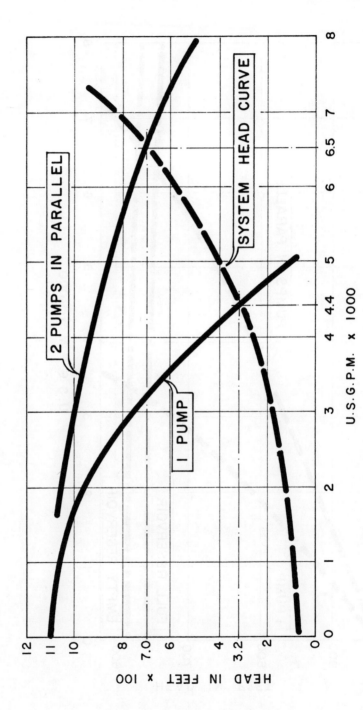

FIGURE.8.   *Steep system head curve with high friction loss.*

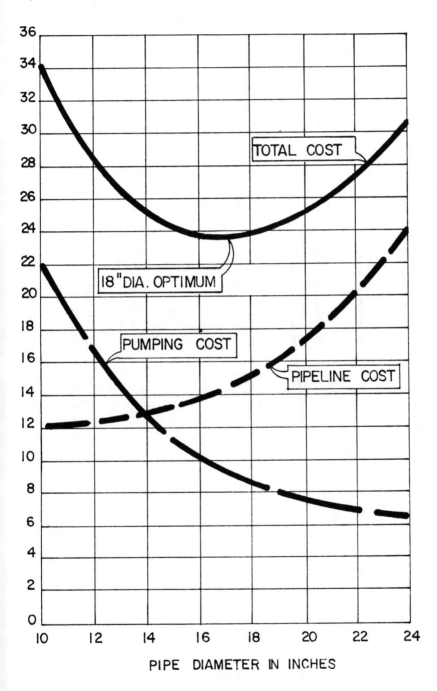

FIGURE 9. *Optimum pipeline diameter.*

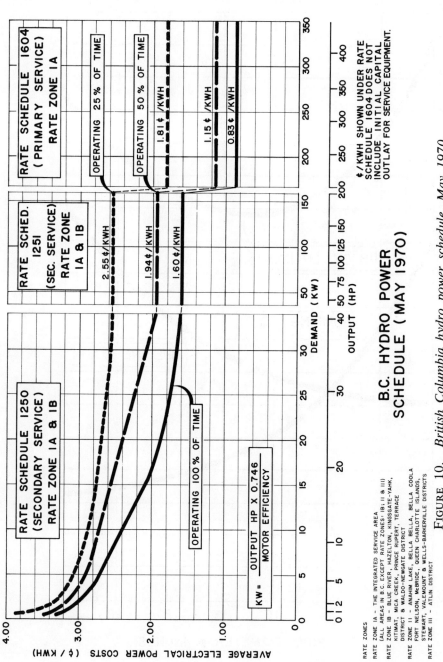

FIGURE 10.   *British Columbia hydro power schedule, May 1970.*

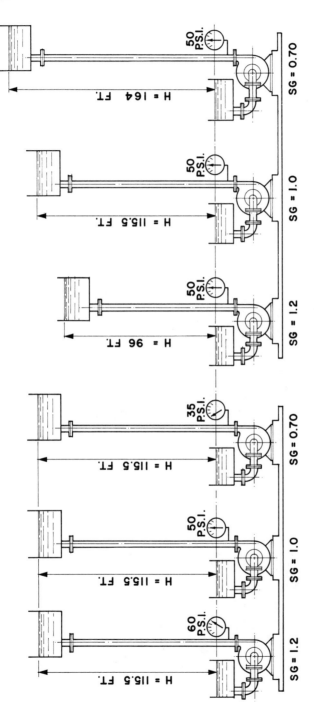

SG = 0.70

SG = 1.0

SG = 1.2

SG = 0.70

SG = 1.0

SG = 1.2

H = 164 FT.

H = 115.5 FT.

H = 96 FT.

H = 115.5 FT.

H = 115.5 FT.

H = 115.5 FT.

50 P.S.I.

50 P.S.I.

50 P.S.I.

35 P.S.I.

50 P.S.I.

60 P.S.I.

FIGURE 11. *Relationship between head, pressure, and special gravity.*

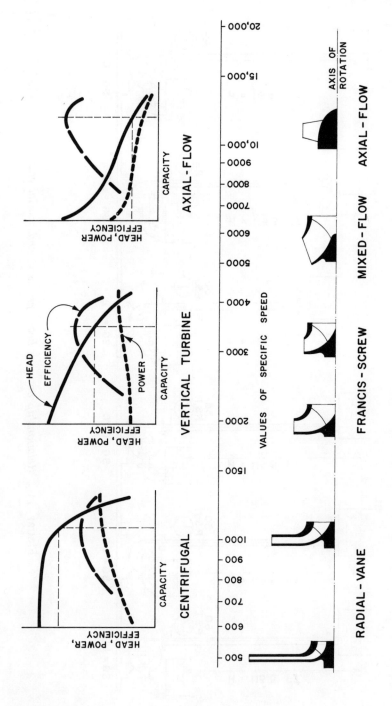

FIGURE 12. *Type characteristics and specific speed scale for various impeller designs.*

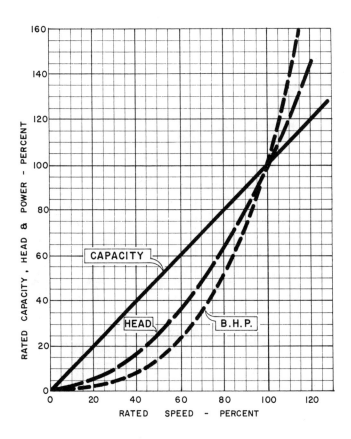

FIGURE 13. *Affinity laws: chart showing effect of speed change on centrifugal pump performance.*

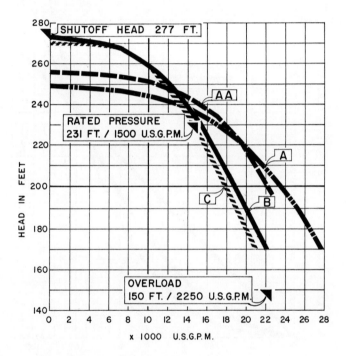

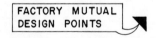

FIGURE 14. *Three typical fire pump curves.*

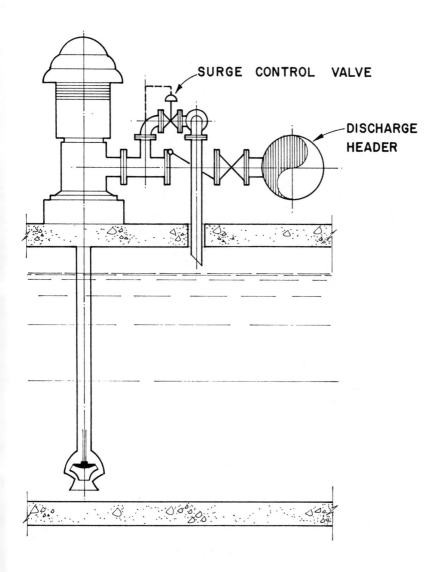

FIGURE 15. *Surge control valve.*

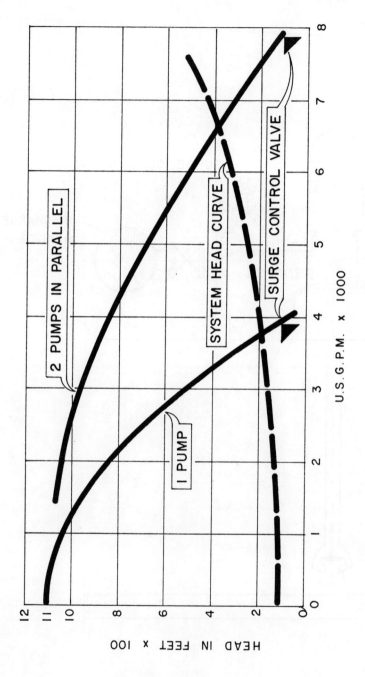

FIGURE 16. *Surge control valve setting.*

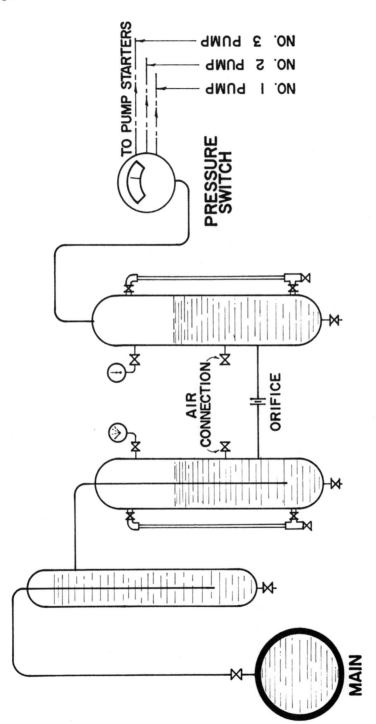

FIGURE 17. *Hydraulic surge suppressor.*

APPENDIX 2
Typical Pump Data Sheets

TYPICAL PUMP DATA SHEETS

To avoid possible misunderstandings, the Engineer should provide a form on which each tenderer can submit his prices.

If this is not done, there is a possibility that quotations will be received as lump sum prices making them very difficult to evaluate. A typical example for a fire pump station is shown.

Example

SCHEDULE OF PRICES - FIRE PUMPS

The tenderer shall supply and deliver to _____, the following equipment at the prices quoted.

The prices shall be exclusive of Federal and Provincial sales taxes. Individual unit prices shall be shown for each numbered item.

Item	Description	Quantity	Unit Price	Extension	Delivery (weeks)
1.	Electric motor driven fire pump	1	_____	_____	_____
2.	Diesel engine driven fire pumps	2	_____	_____	_____
3.	Controller for electric fire pump	1	_____	_____	_____
4.	Controller for diesel fire pump	2	_____	_____	_____
	TOTAL TENDER PRICE			$_____	

Data Sheets

The tenderer shall supply the following data.

FIRE PUMPS

FIRE PUMP

1.   Manufacturer _____

2.   Place of manufacture _____

3.   Delivery of complete units after
      receipt of order (weeks)   _____

4.   Model number and type   _____

5.   Number of stages   _____

6.   Impeller diameter (inches)   _____

7.   Horsepower requirements

      (a) at shut-off head   _____

      (b) at specified head   _____

      (c) at maximum horsepower conditions _____

8.   Efficiency at specified head   _____

9.   Suction diameter (inches)   _____

10.   Discharge diameter (inches)   _____

11.   Weight

      (a) weight of pump c/w motor (lb) _____

      (b) weight of pump c/w engine (lb) _____

12.   Flexible coupling
      Manufacturer and Model No.

      (a) pump with motor drive   _____

      (b) pump with engine drive   _____

13.   Bed plate (cast or fabricated)   _____

Performance Curves

      The supplier is required to submit signed performance curves with
the tender indicating head, capacity, efficiency, horsepower and NPSH.

Pump Drawing

      The tenderer shall submit a line drawing of the completed units (a)
pump with electric motor drive (b) pump with diesel engine drive, showing
all salient dimensions including fuel connections, cooling water connections, exhaust pipe, etc.

FIRE PUMP MOTOR

1. Manufacturer _____

2. Place of manufacture _____

3. Type   _____

4. Horsepower   _____

5. Duty   _____

6. Voltage   _____

7. Phase   _____

8. Frequency   _____

9. Full load speed   _____

10. CEMA frame size   _____

11. Power factor in percent
    (at 100% load)   _____

12. Efficiency in percent
    (at 100% load)   _____

13. Current

    at rated load   _____

    at locked rotor   _____

14. Ambient temperature   _____

15. (a) Insulation class   _____

    (b) Description of insulation system _____

16. Temperature rise at full load   _____

17. CEMA design   _____

    Torque starting % FL   _____

    Breakdown % FL   _____

18. Enclosure   _____

19. Recommended spare parts list   _____

FIRE PUMP DIESEL ENGINE

1. Manufacturer _____

2. Place of manufacture _____

3. Bore and stroke (inches)   _____

4. Number of cylinders   _____

5. Piston displacement (cu ins)   _____

6. Bearings

    (a) crankshaft (No. and dia)   _____

    (b) camshaft (No. and dia)   _____

7. Electrical equipment

    (a) voltage   _____

    (b) generator   _____

    (c) battery capacity   _____

    (d) number of batteries   _____

8. Horsepower

    (at _____ feet above sea level)   _____

    Factory Mutual rating at 1750 rpm

    (bhp)   _____

    Underwriters Laboratories of Canada

    rating (at 1750 rpm) (bhp)   _____

9. Rotation

    when viewed from the opposite end
    of the drive shaft   _____

CONTROLLER FOR ELECTRIC FIRE PUMP

1. Manufacturer _____

2. Place of manufacture _____

3. Type and Model No.   _____

4. Voltage   _____

5. Phase   _____

6. Frequency   _____

CONTROLLER FOR DIESEL FIRE PUMP

1.   Manufacturer _____

2.   Place of manufacture _____

3.   Type and Model No.   _____

4.   Voltage   _____

5.   Phase   _____

6.   Frequency   _____

The supplier is required to submit dimensional line drawings and illustrated literature of all controllers and associated equipment showing connections between the controllers and pumping units.

VERTICAL TURBINE PUMPS

1.   Manufacturer _____

2.   Place of manufacture _____

3.   Delivery after receipt of
      approved shop drawings (weeks)   _____

4.   Model number or type   _____

5.   Shaft speed (rpm)   _____

6.   Specific speed, N_s _____

7.   Number of stages   _____

8.   Impeller diameters: _____

9.   Head developed, each impeller (ft)   _____

10.   Required NPSH (ft)   _____

11.   Required submergence above suction
       bell (ft)   _____

12.   Diameter of suction bell (ft)   _____

13.   Horsepower requirements:

      (a)   at shut-off head   _____

      (b)   at specified head and capacity   _____

      (c)   at maximum horsepower condition   _____

14.   Maximum thrust throughout operating
       range   _____

15.   Efficiency at specified flow and
       head   _____

16.   Discharge flange diameter (in)   _____

17. Weight of pump   _____

18. Weight of motor   _____

19. Weight of completed unit   _____

20. Type of shaft bearings   _____

21. Number of bearings   _____

22. Shaft diameter (in)   _____

23. WR^2 of impellers and shaft ($lb\text{-}ft^2$)   _____

24. Materials of construction:

    (a) Pump base and
         discharge head _____ Specification _____

    (b) Column   _____ Specification _____

    (c) Bowl assembly   _____ Specification _____

    (d) Impellers   _____ Specification _____

    (e) Shafts   _____ Specification _____

    (f) Bearings   _____ Specification _____

    (g) Stuffing box
         bearing   _____ Specification _____

    (h) Impeller wear
         rings   _____ Specification _____

    (i) Coupling   _____ Specification _____

    (j) Coupling bolts   _____ Specification _____

25. Stuffing Box:

    (a) Number of turns of packing   _____

    (b) Type, size, and make of packing   _____

    (c) Number of lantern rings   _____

    (d) Lantern ring material   _____

    (e) Stuffing box gland: solid   _____

                     split   _____

                     material   _____

    (f) Gland studs material   _____

    (g) Gland nuts material   _____

26. Diameter of hole required in floor   _____

Performance Curves

The supplier is required to submit signed performance curves with
this tender indicating head, capacity, efficiency, horsepower, and NPSH.

Pump Drawing

       The tenderer shall submit a line drawing of the completed unit showing all salient dimensions. Illustrated literature shall be provided to indicate specific features.

MOTOR FOR VERTICAL TURBINE PUMPS

1.   Manufacturer _____

2.   Place of manufacture _____

3.   Delivery after receipt of
approved shop drawings (weeks)   _____

4.   Type   _____

5.   hp   _____

6.   Duty   _____

7.   Continuous service factor   _____

8.   Voltage   _____

9.   Phase   _____

10.   Frequency   _____

11.   Full load speed   _____

12.   Maximum overspeed in each direction   _____

13.   CEMA frame size   _____

14.   Power factor in percent:

      at 80% load _____   at 95% load _____

      at 85% load _____   at 100% load _____

      at 90% load _____   at 105% load _____

15.   Efficiency in percent:

      at 80% load _____   at 95% load _____

      at 85% load _____   at 100% load _____

      at 90% load _____   at 105% load _____

16.   Current: at full load   _____

             at locked rotor   _____

17.   Ambient temperature   _____

18.   (a) Insulation class   _____

      (b) Description of insulation system _____

19.   Temperature rise at full load   _____

20.   CEMA design   _____

21. Torque: starting (% full load)   _____

         breakdown (% full load)   _____

22. Maximum vibration   _____

23. Sound level at rated speed   _____

24. Bearing type: top   _____

                  bottom   _____

25. (a) Bearing average life   _____

     (b) Normal bearing operating
          temperature (°C)   _____

26. Thrust capacity: up   _____

                    down   _____

27. Anti-condensation heaters:

            quantity   _____

            kw each   _____

            voltage   _____

            phase   _____

28. Enclosure   _____

29. Type of stator temperature indicator   _____

30. Type of stator temperature alarm
     switches   _____

31. Type of main bearing temperature
     relay   _____

32. Quantity of main bearing temperature
     relays   _____

33. Type of vibration detector   _____

34. Quantity of connection boxes   _____

35. Painting finish   _____

36. Permissible number of starts per hour _____

APPENDIX 3
Typical Maintenance Data Sheet

TYPICAL MAINTENANCE DATA SHEET

PUMP

Make _____   Supplier _____

Agent _____   Size and Type _____

Serial _____   Model _____

Date Installed _____   Instruction Manual _____

Pump Rating

Capacity _____ USgpm   Shaft speed _____ rpm

Head _____ ft   Shutoff head _____ ft

Number of stages _____   Direction of rotation _____

Impeller diameter _____   Performance curve number _____

Stuffing Box/Mechanical Seal

Size: OD _____   ID _____

Packing manufacturer _____

Number of packing rings _____

Size of rings _____

Manufacturer of seal _____

Model number _____   Type _____

Serial number _____   Size _____

Item	Material Specification	Part Number
Casing	_____	_____
Bowl assembly	_____	_____
Impellers	_____	_____
Impeller rings	_____	_____

Item	Material Specification	Part Number
Casing rings	_____	_____
shaft	_____	_____
Shaft sleeves	_____	_____
Stuffing box bushing	_____	_____
Gland	_____	_____
Impeller nut	_____	_____
Gasket material	_____	_____
Shaft bearings	_____	_____
Coupling	_____	_____

DRIVER

Make _____   Supplier _____

Agent _____   Size and type _____

Serial _____   Model _____

Date Installed _____   Instruction manual _____

hp _____ rpm _____ Frame _____

Volts _____ Phases _____ Cycles _____

Number of cylinders _____ Bore and stroke _____

For details of nomenclature see Hydraulic Institute Standards.[2]

MAINTENANCE RECORD

Date inspected _____

Inspected by _____

Repairs _____

_____

Repaired by _____

New parts installed _____

_____

Cost of repairs _____

_____

Down time _____

_____

Remarks _____

_____

_____

_____

_____

APPENDIX 4
Velocity Tables

NOTE: Tables I and II are included to facilitate conversion from US gallons to imperial gallons for use with Figure 6 (Universal Pipe
Friction Diagram, following page 51) and the velocity tables,
both of which are calculated in imperial gallons. The conversion
tables are based on the following:

$$1 \text{ imperial gallon} = 1.20095 \text{ US gallons}$$
$$1 \text{ US gallon} \quad = 0.832675 \text{ imperial gallon}$$

TABLE I: CONVERSION FROM IGPM TO USGPM

IGPM	USGPM	IGPM	USGPM	IGPM	USGPM	IGPM	USGPM
1.0	1.2009	130	156.12	3,400	4,083.2	34,000	40,832.3
1.5	1.8014	140	168.13	3,600	4,323.4	35,000	42,033.3
2.0	2.4019	150	180.14	3,800	4,563.6	36,000	43,234.2
2.5	3.0024	160	192.15	4,000	4,803.8	37,000	44,435.2
3.0	3.6029	170	204.16	4,500	5,404.3	38,000	45,636.1
4	4.8038	180	216.17	5,000	6,004.8	39,000	46,837.1
5	6.0048	190	228.18	5,500	6,605.2	40,000	48,038.0
6	7.2057	200	240.19	6,000	7,205.7	41,000	49,239.0
7	8.4067	220	264.21	6,500	7,806.2	42,000	50,439.9
8	9.6076	240	288.23	7,000	8,406.7	43,000	51,640.9
9	10.809	260	312.25	7,500	9,007.1	44,000	52,841.8
10	12.009	280	336.27	8,000	9,607.6	45,000	54,042.8
11	13.210	300	360.29	8,500	10,208.1	46,000	55,243.7
12	14.411	320	384.30	9,000	10,808.6	47,000	56,444.7
13	15.612	340	408.32	9,500	11,409.0	48,000	57,645.6
14	16.813	360	432.34	10,000	12,009.5	49,000	58,846.6
15	18.014	380	456.36	10,500	12,610.0	50,000	60,047.5
16	19.215	400	480.38	11,000	13,210.5	52,000	62,449.4
17	20.416	420	504.40	11,500	13,810.9	54,000	64,851.3
18	21.617	440	528.42	12,000	14,411.4	56,000	67,253.2
19	22.818	460	552.44	12,500	15,011.9	58,000	69,655.1
20	24.019	480	576.46	13,000	15,612.4	60,000	72,057.0
22	26.421	500	600.48	13,500	16,212.8	62,000	74,458.9
24	28.823	550	660.52	14,000	16,813.3	64,000	76,860.8
26	31.225	600	720.57	14,500	17,413.8	66,000	79,262.7
28	33.627	650	780.62	15,000	18,014.3	68,000	81,664.6
30	36.029	700	840.67	15,500	18,614.7	70,000	84,066.5
32	38.430	750	900.71	16,000	19,215.2	75,000	90,071.3
34	40.832	800	960.76	16,500	19,815.7	80,000	96,076
36	43.234	850	1,020.8	17,000	20,416.2	85,000	102,081
38	45.636	900	1,080.9	17,500	21,016.6	90,000	108,086
40	48.038	950	1,140.9	18,000	21,617.1	95,000	114,090
42	50.440	1,000	1,200.9	18,500	22,217.6	100,000	120,095
44	52.842	1,100	1,321.0	19,000	22,818.1	110,000	132,104
46	55.244	1,200	1,441.1	19,500	23,418.5	120,000	144,114
48	57.646	1,300	1,561.2	20,000	24,019.0	130,000	156,124
50	60.048	1,400	1,681.3	21,000	25,220.0	140,000	168,133
55	66.052	1,500	1,801.4	22,000	26,420.9	150,000	180,143
60	72.057	1,600	1,921.5	23,000	27,621.9	160,000	192,152
65	78.062	1,700	2,041.6	24,000	28,822.8	170,000	204,162
70	84.067	1,800	2,161.7	25,000	30,023.8	180,000	216,171
75	90.071	1,900	2,281.8	26,000	31,224.7	190,000	228,181
80	96.076	2,000	2,401.9	27,000	32,425.7	200,000	240,190
85	102.08	2,200	2,642.1	28,000	33,626.6	210,000	252,200
90	108.09	2,400	2,882.3	29,000	34,827.6	220,000	264,209
95	114.09	2,600	3,122.5	30,000	36,028.5	230,000	276,219
100	120.09	2,800	3,362.7	31,000	37,229.5	240,000	288,228
110	132.10	3,000	3,602.9	32,000	38,430.4	250,000	300,238
120	144.11	3,200	3,843.0	33,000	39,631.4		

Pump Selection

TABLE II: CONVERSION FROM USGPM TO IGPM

USGPM	IGPM	USGPM	IGPM	USGPM	IGPM	USGPM	IGPM
1.0	0.8327	140	116.57	3,800	3,164.2	37,000	30,809.0
1.5	1.2490	150	124.90	4,000	3,330.7	38,000	31,641.7
2.0	1.6654	160	133.23	4,500	3,747.0	39,000	32,474.3
2.5	2.0817	170	141.55	5,000	4,163.4	40,000	33,307.0
3	2.4980	180	149.88	5,500	4,579.7	41,000	34,139.7
4	3.3307	190	158.21	6,000	4,996.1	42,000	34,972.4
5	4.1634	200	166.54	6,500	5,412.4	43,000	35,805.0
6	4.9961	220	183.19	7,000	5,828.7	44,000	36,637.7
7	5.8287	240	199.84	7,500	6,245.1	45,000	37,470.4
8	6.6614	260	216.50	8,000	6,661.4	46,000	38,303.1
9	7.4941	280	233.15	8,500	7,077.7	47,000	39,135.7
10	8.3268	300	249.80	9,000	7,494.1	48,000	39,968.4
11	9.1594	320	266.46	9,500	7,910.4	49,000	40,801.1
12	9.9921	340	283.11	10,000	8,326.8	50,000	41,633.8
13	10.825	360	299.76	10,500	8,743.1	52,000	43,299.1
14	11.657	380	316.42	11,000	9,159.4	54,000	44,964.5
15	12.490	400	333.07	11,500	9,575.8	56,000	46,629.8
16	13.323	420	349.72	12,000	9,992.1	58,000	48,295.2
17	14.155	440	366.38	12,500	10,408.4	60,000	49,960.5
18	14.988	460	383.03	13,000	10,824.8	62,000	51,625.9
19	15.821	480	399.68	13,500	11,241.1	64,000	53,291.2
20	16.654	500	416.34	14,000	11,657.5	66,000	54,956.6
22	18.319	550	457.97	14,500	12,073.8	68,000	56,621.9
24	19.984	600	499.61	15,000	12,490.1	70,000	58,287.3
26	21.650	650	541.24	15,500	12,906.5	75,000	62,450.6
28	23.315	700	582.87	16,000	13,322.8	80,000	66,614.0
30	24.980	750	624.51	16,500	13,739.1	85,000	70,777.4
32	26.646	800	666.14	17,000	14,155.5	90,000	74,940.8
34	28.311	850	707.77	17,500	14,571.8	95,000	79,104.1
36	29.976	900	749.41	18,000	14,988.2	100,000	83,267.5
38	31.642	950	791.04	18,500	15,404.5	110,000	91,594.3
40	33.307	1,000	832.68	19,000	15,820.8	120,000	99,921.0
42	34.972	1,100	915.94	19,500	16,237.2	130,000	108,248
44	36.638	1,200	999.21	20,000	16,653.5	140,000	116,575
46	38.303	1,300	1,082.5	21,000	17,486.2	150,000	124,901
48	39.968	1,400	1,165.7	22,000	18,318.9	160,000	133,228
50	41.634	1,500	1,249.0	23,000	19,151.5	170,000	141,555
55	45.797	1,600	1,332.3	24,000	19,984.2	180,000	149,882
60	49.961	1,700	1,415.5	25,000	20,816.9	190,000	158,208
65	54.124	1,800	1,498.8	26,000	21,649.6	200,000	166,535
70	58.287	1,900	1,582.1	27,000	22,482.2	210,000	174,862
75	62.451	2,000	1,665.4	28,000	23,314.9	220,000	183,189
80	66.614	2,200	1,831.9	29,000	24,147.6	230,000	191,515
85	70.777	2,400	1,998.4	30,000	24,980.3	240,000	199,842
90	74.941	2,600	2.165.0	31,000	25,812.9	250,000	208,169
95	79.104	2,800	2,331.5	32,000	26,645.6	260,000	216,496
100	83.268	3,000	2,498.0	33,000	27,478.3	270,000	224,822
110	91.594	3,200	2,664.6	34,000	28,311.0	280,000	233,149
120	99.921	3,400	2,831.1	35,000	29,143.6	290,000	241,476
130	108.25	3,600	2,997.6	36,000	29,976.3	300,000	249,803

KEY TO VELOCITY TABLES

	INTERNAL DIAMETER OF PIPE IN INCHES			
FLOW IN I.G.P.M.	1 — 20	21 — 40	41 — 60	61 — 72
1	A 1			
18				
19	A 2			
65				
70	A 3	B 3		
260				
280	A 4	B 4	C 4	D 4
900				
950	A 5	B 5	C 5	D 5
2,800				
2,900	A 6	B 6	C 6	D 6
10,500				
11,000	A 7	B 7	C 7	D 7
21,000				
22,000	A 8	B 8	C 8	D 8
41,000				
42,000		B 9	C 9	D 9
75,000				
80,000		B 10	C 10	D 10
250,000				

NOTE: INTERNAL DIAMETER IN INCHES ARE ACTUAL DIAMETERS AND NOT NOMINAL DIAMETERS.

VELOCITY IN FEET PER SECOND.

A-1

IGPM	1"	2"	3"	4"	5"	6"	7"	8"	9"	10"	11"	12"	13"	14"	15"	16"	17"	18"	19"	20"
1	.486	.123	.055	.031																
1.5	.730	.184	.082	.046																
2	.973	.246	.109	.061																
2.5	1.22	.307	.136	.077																
3	1.46	.368	.164	.092																
4	1.95	.491	.218	.123																
5	2.43	.614	.273	.153	.098	.068														
6	2.92	.736	.327	.184	.118	.082														
7	3.41	.859	.382	.215	.137	.095														
8	3.89	.982	.436	.245	.157	.109														
9	4.38	1.11	.491	.276	.177	.123														
10	4.86	1.23	.545	.306	.196	.136	.100	.0766												
11	5.35	1.35	.599	.337	.216	.150	.110	.084												
12	5.84	1.47	.654	.368	.235	.164	.120	.092												
13	6.32	1.60	.708	.398	.255	.177	.130	.099												
14	6.81	1.72	.763	.429	.275	.191	.140	.107												
15	7.30	1.84	.817	.460	.294	.204	.150	.115	.091											
16	7.78	1.96	.872	.490	.314	.218	.160	.123	.097											
17	8.27	2.09	.926	.521	.333	.232	.170	.130	.103											
18	8.76	2.21	.981	.552	.353	.245	.180	.138	.109											

DIAMETER OF PIPE IN INCHES.

VELOCITY IN FEET PER SECOND.

DIAMETER OF PIPE IN INCHES.

IGPM	1"	2"	3"	4"	5"	6"	7"	8"	9"	10"	11"	12"	13"	14"	15"	16"	17"	18"	19"	20"
19	9.24	2.33	1.04	.582	.373	.259	.190	.146	.115											
20	9.73	2.46	1.09	.613	.392	.273	.200	.153	.121	.0981										
22	10.7	2.70	1.20	.674	.432	.300	.220	.169	.133	.108										
24	11.7	2.95	1.31	.736	.471	.327	.240	.184	.145	.118	.097	.082								
26	12.7	3.19	1.42	.797	.510	.354	.260	.199	.157	.128	.105	.088								
28	13.6	3.44	1.53	.858	.549	.382	.280	.215	.170	.137	.114	.095								
30	14.6	3.68	1.64	.920	.589	.409	.300	.230	.182	.147	.122	.102	.0871	.0751						
32	15.6	3.93	1.74	.981	.628	.436	.320	.245	.194	.157	.130	.109	.093	.080						
34	16.5	4.17	1.85	1.04	.667	.463	.340	.261	.206	.167	.138	.116	.099	.085						
36	17.5	4.42	1.96	1.10	.706	.491	.361	.276	.218	.177	.146	.123	.105	.090						
38	18.5	4.66	2.07	1.16	.745	.518	.381	.291	.230	.186	.154	.129	.110	.095	.083					
40	19.5	4.91	2.18	1.23	.785	.545	.401	.307	.242	.196	.162	.136	.116	.100	.087					
42	20.4	5.15	2.29	1.29	.824	.572	.421	.322	.254	.206	.170	.143	.122	.105	.092					
44	21.4	5.40	2.40	1.35	.863	.600	.441	.337	.266	.216	.178	.150	.128	.110	.096					
46	22.4	5.65	2.51	1.41	.902	.627	.461	.353	.279	.226	.187	.157	.134	.115	.100	.088				
48	23.4	5.89	2.62	1.47	.942	.654	.481	.368	.291	.235	.197	.164	.139	.120	.105	.092				
50	24.3	6.14	2.73	1.53	.981	.682	.501	.383	.303	.245	.203	.170	.145	.125	.109	.096	.085			
55		6.75	3.00	1.69	1.08	.750	.551	.422	.333	.270	.223	.187	.160	.138	.120	.105	.094	.083		
60		7.36	3.27	1.84	1.18	.818	.601	.460	.363	.294	.243	.204	.174	.150	.131	.115	.102	.091		
65		7.98	3.54	1.99	1.28	.886	.651	.498	.394	.319	.264	.221	.189	.163	.142	.125	.110	.098	.088	

A-3

VELOCITY IN FEET PER SECOND.

DIAMETER OF PIPE IN INCHES.

IGPM	1"	2"	3"	4"	5"	6"	7"	8"	9"	10"	11"	12"	13"	14"	15"	16"	17"	18"	19"	20"
70		8.59	3.82	2.15	1.37	.954	.701	.537	.424	.343	.284	.238	.203	.175	.153	.134	.119	.106	.095	.086
75		9.21	4.09	2.30	1.47	1.02	.751	.575	.454	.368	.304	.255	.218	.188	.163	.143	.127	.114	.102	.092
80		9.82	4.36	2.45	1.57	1.09	.801	.613	.485	.392	.324	.273	.232	.200	.174	.153	.136	.121	.109	.098
85		10.4	4.63	2.61	1.67	1.16	.851	.651	.515	.417	.345	.290	.247	.213	.185	.162	.144	.129	.116	.104
90		11.1	4.91	2.76	1.77	1.23	.901	.690	.545	.442	.365	.307	.261	.225	.196	.172	.152	.136	.122	.110
95		11.7	5.18	2.91	1.86	1.29	.951	.728	.575	.466	.385	.324	.276	.238	.207	.182	.162	.144	.129	.117
100		12.3	5.45	3.07	1.96	1.36	1.00	.766	.606	.491	.405	.341	.290	.250	.218	.192	.170	.151	.136	.123
110		13.5	5.99	3.37	2.16	1.50	1.10	.843	.666	.540	.446	.375	.319	.275	.240	.211	.187	.167	.149	.135
120		14.7	6.54	3.68	2.35	1.64	1.20	.920	.727	.589	.487	.409	.348	.300	.262	.230	.204	.182	.163	.147
130		16.0	7.08	3.98	2.55	1.77	1.30	.996	.787	.638	.527	.443	.377	.325	.283	.249	.221	.197	.177	.159
140		17.2	7.63	4.29	2.75	1.91	1.40	1.07	.848	.687	.568	.477	.406	.350	.305	.268	.238	.212	.190	.172
150		18.4	8.17	4.60	2.94	2.04	1.50	1.15	.908	.736	.608	.511	.435	.375	.327	.287	.255	.227	.204	.184
160		19.6	8.72	4.90	3.14	2.18	1.60	1.23	.969	.785	.649	.545	.465	.400	.349	.307	.272	.242	.217	.196
170		20.1	9.26	5.21	3.33	2.32	1.70	1.30	1.03	.834	.689	.579	.494	.426	.371	.326	.289	.257	.231	.208
180		22.1	9.81	5.52	3.53	2.45	1.80	1.38	1.09	.883	.730	.613	.523	.451	.392	.345	.306	.273	.245	.221
190		23.3	10.4	5.82	3.73	2.59	1.90	1.46	1.15	.932	.770	.647	.552	.476	.414	.364	.323	.288	.258	.233
200		24.5	10.9	6.13	3.92	2.73	2.00	1.53	1.21	.981	.811	.681	.581	.501	.436	.383	.339	.303	.272	.245
220			12.0	6.74	4.32	3.00	2.20	1.69	1.33	1.08	.892	.749	.639	.551	.480	.422	.373	.333	.299	.270
240			13.1	7.36	4.71	3.27	2.40	1.84	1.45	1.18	.973	.818	.697	.601	.523	.460	.407	.363	.326	.294
260			14.2	7.97	5.10	3.54	2.60	1.99	1.57	1.28	1.05	.886	.755	.651	.567	.498	.441	.394	.353	.319

VELOCITY IN FEET PER SECOND.

DIAMETER OF PIPE IN INCHES.

IGPM	1"	2"	3"	4"	5"	6"	7"	8"	9"	10"	11"	12"	13"	14"	15"	16"	17"	18"	19"	20"
280			15.3	8.58	5.49	3.82	2.80	2.15	1.70	1.37	1.14	.954	.813	.701	.610	.537	.475	.424	.380	.343
300			16.3	9.20	5.89	4.09	3.00	2.30	1.82	1.47	1.22	1.02	.871	.751	.654	.575	.509	.454	.408	.368
320			17.4	9.81	6.28	4.36	3.20	2.45	1.94	1.57	1.30	1.09	.929	.801	.698	.613	.543	.485	.435	.392
340			18.5	10.4	6.67	4.63	3.40	2.61	2.06	1.67	1.38	1.16	.987	.851	.741	.652	.577	.515	.462	.417
360			19.6	11.0	7.06	4.91	3.61	2.76	2.18	1.77	1.46	1.23	1.05	.901	.785	.690	.611	.545	.489	.442
380			20.7	11.6	7.45	5.18	3.81	2.91	2.30	1.86	1.54	1.29	1.10	.951	.828	.728	.645	.575	.516	.466
400			21.8	12.3	7.85	5.45	4.01	3.07	2.42	1.96	1.62	1.36	1.16	1.00	.872	.767	.679	.606	.544	.491
420			22.9	12.9	8.24	5.72	4.21	3.22	2.54	2.06	1.70	1.43	1.22	1.05	.916	.805	.713	.636	.571	.515
440			24.0	13.5	8.63	6.00	4.41	3.37	2.66	2.16	1.78	1.50	1.28	1.10	.959	.843	.747	.666	.598	.540
460			25.1	14.1	9.02	6.27	4.61	3.53	2.79	2.26	1.87	1.57	1.34	1.15	1.00	.881	.781	.697	.625	.564
480			26.2	14.7	9.42	6.54	4.81	3.68	2.91	2.35	1.95	1.64	1.39	1.20	1.05	.920	.815	.727	.653	.589
500			27.2	15.3	9.81	6.82	5.01	3.83	3.03	2.45	2.03	1.70	1.45	1.25	1.09	.958	.849	.757	.679	.613
550				16.9	10.8	7.50	5.51	4.22	3.33	2.70	2.23	1.87	1.60	1.38	1.20	1.05	.934	.833	.747	.675
600				18.4	11.8	8.18	6.01	4.60	3.63	2.94	2.43	2.04	1.74	1.50	1.31	1.15	1.02	.909	.815	.736
650				19.9	12.8	8.86	6.51	4.98	3.94	3.19	2.64	2.21	1.89	1.63	1.42	1.25	1.10	.984	.883	.797
700				21.5	13.7	9.54	7.01	5.37	4.24	3.43	2.84	2.38	2.03	1.75	1.53	1.34	1.19	1.06	.951	.858
750				23.0	14.7	10.2	7.51	5.75	4.54	3.68	3.04	2.55	2.18	1.88	1.63	1.43	1.27	1.14	1.02	.920
800				24.5	15.7	10.9	8.01	6.13	4.85	3.92	3.24	2.73	2.32	2.00	1.74	1.53	1.36	1.21	1.09	.981
850				26.1	16.7	11.6	8.51	6.51	5.15	4.17	3.45	2.90	2.47	2.13	1.85	1.62	1.44	1.29	1.16	1.04
900				27.6	17.7	12.3	9.01	6.90	5.45	4.42	3.65	3.07	2.61	2.25	1.96	1.72	1.52	1.36	1.22	1.10

VELOCITY IN FEET PER SECOND.

A-5

IGPM	1"	2"	3"	4"	5"	6"	7"	8"	9"	10"	11"	12"	13"	14"	15"	16"	17"	18"	19"	20"
950				29.1	18.6	12.9	9.51	7.28	5.75	4.66	3.85	3.24	2.76	2.38	2.07	1.82	1.61	1.44	1.29	1.17
1000				30.7	19.6	13.6	10.0	7.66	6.06	4.91	4.05	3.41	2.90	2.50	2.18	1.92	1.70	1.51	1.36	1.23
1100				33.7	21.6	15.0	11.0	8.43	6.66	5.40	4.46	3.75	3.19	2.75	2.40	2.11	1.87	1.67	1.49	1.35
1200				36.8	23.5	16.4	12.0	9.20	7.27	5.89	4.87	4.09	3.48	3.00	2.62	2.30	2.04	1.82	1.63	1.47
1300				39.8	25.5	17.7	13.0	9.96	7.87	6.38	5.27	4.43	3.77	3.25	2.83	2.49	2.21	1.97	1.77	1.59
1400				42.9	27.5	19.1	14.0	10.7	8.48	6.87	5.68	4.77	4.06	3.50	3.05	2.68	2.38	2.12	1.90	1.72
1500				46.0	29.4	20.4	15.0	11.5	9.08	7.36	6.08	5.11	4.35	3.75	3.27	2.87	2.55	2.27	2.04	1.84
1600					31.4	21.8	16.0	12.3	9.69	7.85	6.49	5.45	4.65	4.00	3.49	3.07	2.72	2.42	2.17	1.96
1700						23.2	17.0	13.0	10.3	8.34	6.89	5.79	4.94	4.26	3.71	3.26	2.89	2.57	2.31	2.08
1800						24.5	18.0	13.8	10.9	8.83	7.30	6.13	5.23	4.51	3.92	3.45	3.06	2.73	2.45	2.21
1900						25.9	19.0	14.6	11.5	9.32	7.70	6.47	5.52	4.76	4.14	3.64	3.23	2.88	2.58	2.33
2000						27.3	20.0	15.3	12.1	9.81	8.11	6.81	5.81	5.01	4.36	3.83	3.39	3.03	2.72	2.45
2100						28.6	21.0	16.1	12.7	10.3	8.51	7.15	6.10	5.26	4.58	4.02	3.56	3.18	2.85	2.58
2200						30.0	22.0	16.9	13.3	10.8	8.92	7.49	6.39	5.51	4.80	4.22	3.73	3.33	2.99	2.70
2300						31.4	23.0	17.6	13.9	11.3	9.33	7.84	6.68	5.76	5.01	4.41	3.90	3.48	3.13	2.82
2400						32.7	24.0	18.4	14.5	11.8	9.73	8.18	6.97	6.01	5.23	4.60	4.07	3.63	3.26	2.94
2500						34.1	25.0	19.2	15.1	12.3	10.1	8.52	7.26	6.26	5.45	4.78	4.24	3.78	3.40	3.07
2600							26.0	19.9	15.7	12.8	10.5	8.86	7.55	6.51	5.67	4.98	4.41	3.94	3.53	3.19
2700							27.0	20.7	16.4	13.2	10.9	9.20	7.84	6.76	5.88	5.17	4.58	4.09	3.67	3.31
2800							28.0	21.5	17.0	13.7	11.4	9.54	8.13	7.01	6.10	5.37	4.75	4.24	3.80	3.43

DIAMETER OF PIPE IN INCHES.

A-6

VELOCITY IN FEET PER SECOND.

DIAMETER OF PIPE IN INCHES.

IGPM	1"	2"	3"	4"	5"	6"	7"	8"	9"	10"	11"	12"	13"	14"	15"	16"	17"	18"	19"	20"
2900							29.0	22.2	17.6	14.2	11.8	9.88	8.42	7.26	6.32	5.56	4.92	4.39	3.94	3.56
3000							30.0	23.0	18.2	14.7	12.2	10.2	8.71	7.51	6.54	5.75	5.09	4.54	4.08	3.68
3200								24.5	19.4	15.7	13.0	10.9	9.29	8.01	6.98	6.13	5.43	4.85	4.35	3.92
3400								26.1	20.6	16.7	13.8	11.6	9.87	8.51	7.41	6.52	5.77	5.15	4.62	4.17
3600								27.6	21.8	17.7	14.6	12.3	10.5	9.01	7.85	6.90	6.11	5.45	4.89	4.42
3800								29.1	23.0	18.6	15.4	12.9	11.0	9.51	8.29	7.28	6.45	5.75	5.16	4.66
4000								30.7	24.2	19.6	16.2	13.6	11.6	10.0	8.72	7.67	6.79	6.06	5.44	4.91
4500									27.3	22.1	18.2	15.3	13.1	11.3	9.81	8.62	7.64	6.81	6.12	5.52
5000									30.3	24.5	20.3	17.0	14.5	12.5	10.9	9.58	8.49	7.57	6.79	6.13
5500									33.3	27.0	22.3	18.7	16.0	13.8	12.0	10.5	9.34	8.33	7.47	6.75
6000									36.3	29.4	24.3	20.4	17.4	15.0	13.1	11.5	10.2	9.09	8.15	7.36
6500										31.9	26.4	22.1	18.9	16.3	14.2	12.5	11.0	9.84	8.83	7.97
7000										34.3	28.4	23.8	20.3	17.5	15.3	13.4	11.9	10.6	9.51	8.58
7500												25.6	21.8	18.8	16.4	14.4	12.7	11.4	10.2	9.20
8000												27.3	23.2	20.0	17.4	15.3	13.6	12.1	10.9	9.81
8500												29.0	24.7	21.3	18.5	16.3	14.4	12.9	11.6	10.4
9000												30.7	26.1	22.5	19.6	17.2	15.3	13.6	12.2	11.0
9500												32.4	27.6	23.8	20.7	18.2	16.1	14.4	12.9	11.7
10000												34.1	29.0	25.0	21.8	19.2	17.0	15.1	13.6	12.3
10500														26.2	22.9	20.1	17.8	15.9	14.3	12.9

VELOCITY IN FEET PER SECOND.

A-7

DIAMETER OF PIPE IN INCHES.

IGPM	1"	2"	3"	4"	5"	6"	7"	8"	9"	10"	11"	12"	13"	14"	15"	16"	17"	18"	19"	20"
11000														27.5	24.0	21.1	18.7	16.7	14.9	13.5
11500															25.1	22.0	19.5	17.4	15.6	14.1
12000															26.2	23.0	20.4	18.2	16.3	14.7
12500															27.2	24.0	21.2	18.9	17.0	15.3
13000															28.3	24.9	22.1	19.7	17.7	15.9
13500															29.4	25.8	22.9	20.4	18.3	16.6
14000															30.5	26.8	23.8	21.2	19.0	17.2
14500															31.6	27.8	24.6	22.0	19.7	17.8
15000															32.7	28.7	25.5	22.7	20.4	18.4
15500																	26.3	23.5	21.1	19.0
16000																	27.2	24.2	21.7	19.6
16500																	28.0	25.0	22.4	20.2
17000																	28.9	25.7	23.1	20.8
17500																	29.7	26.5	23.8	21.5
18000																	30.6	27.3	24.5	22.1
18500																		28.0	25.1	22.7
19000																		28.8	25.8	23.3
19500																		29.5	26.5	23.9
20000																		30.3	27.2	24.5
21000																			28.5	25.8

A-8

VELOCITY IN FEET PER SECOND.

DIAMETER OF PIPE IN INCHES.

IGPM	1"	2"	3"	4"	5"	6"	7"	8"	9"	10"	11"	12"	13"	14"	15"	16"	17"	18"	19"	20"
22000																			29.9	27.0
23000																			31.3	28.2
24000																			32.6	29.4
25000																			34.0	30.7
26000																			35.3	31.9
27000																			36.7	33.1
28000																			38.0	34.3
29000																			39.4	35.6
30000																			40.8	36.8
31000																				
32000																				
33000																				
34000																				
35000																				
36000																				
37000																				
38000																				
39000																				
40000																				
41000																				

VELOCITY IN FEET PER SECOND.

DIAMETER OF PIPE IN INCHES.

B-3

IGPM	21"	22"	23"	24"	25"	26"	27"	28"	29"	30"	31"	32"	33"	34"	35"	36"	37"	38"	39"	40"
70																				
75																				
80	.089																			
85	.095																			
90	.100	.0912																		
95	.106	.0963	.881																	
100	.111	.101	.927	.0852																
110	.122	.111	.102	.0937	.0863															
120	.133	.122	.111	.102	.0942	.0871														
130	.145	.132	.121	.111	.102	.0943	.0875													
140	.156	.142	.130	.119	.110	.102	.0942	.0876												
150	.167	.152	.139	.128	.118	.109	.101	.0939	.0875											
160	.178	.162	.148	.136	.126	.116	.108	.100	.0933	.0927										
170	.189	.172	.158	.145	.133	.123	.114	.106	.0992	.0981										
180	.200	.182	.167	.153	.141	.131	.121	.113	.105	.104	.0919									
190	.211	.193	.176	.162	.149	.138	.128	.119	.111	.109	.097									
200	.222	.203	.185	.170	.157	.145	.135	.125	.117	.120	.107	.0958								
220	.245	.223	.204	.187	.173	.160	.148	.138	.128	.131	.112	.105	.0991	.0881						
240	.267	.243	.223	.204	.188	.174	.162	.150	.140	.142	.123	.115	.108	.0961	.0908					
260	.289	.264	.241	.221	.204	.189	.175	.163	.152		.133	.125	.117	.104	.0984	.0932				

VELOCITY IN FEET PER SECOND.

B-4

IGPM	21"	22"	23"	24"	25"	26"	27"	28"	29"	30"	31"	32"	33"	34"	35"	36"	37"	38"	39"	40"
280	.311	.284	.260	.238	.220	.203	.188	.175	.163	.153	.143	.134	.126	.119	.112	.106	.100	.0951	.0903	
300	.334	.304	.278	.256	.235	.218	.202	.188	.175	.164	.153	.144	.135	.127	.120	.114	.108	.102	.0968	.0920
320	.356	.324	.297	.273	.251	.232	.215	.200	.187	.174	.163	.153	.144	.136	.128	.121	.115	.109	.103	.0981
340	.378	.345	.315	.290	.267	.247	.229	.213	.198	.185	.174	.163	.153	.144	.136	.129	.122	.116	.110	.104
360	.400	.365	.334	.307	.283	.261	.242	.225	.210	.196	.184	.172	.162	.153	.144	.136	.129	.122	.116	.110
380	.423	.385	.352	.324	.298	.276	.256	.238	.222	.207	.194	.182	.171	.161	.152	.144	.136	.129	.123	.117
400	.445	.405	.371	.341	.314	.290	.269	.250	.233	.218	.204	.192	.180	.170	.160	.151	.143	.136	.129	.123
420	.467	.426	.389	.358	.329	.305	.283	.263	.245	.229	.214	.201	.189	.178	.168	.159	.151	.143	.135	.129
440	.490	.446	.408	.375	.345	.319	.297	.275	.257	.240	.225	.211	.198	.187	.176	.167	.158	.149	.142	.135
460	.512	.466	.426	.392	.361	.334	.310	.288	.268	.251	.235	.220	.207	.195	.184	.174	.165	.156	.148	.141
480	.534	.486	.445	.409	.376	.349	.323	.300	.280	.262	.245	.230	.216	.204	.192	.182	.172	.163	.155	.147
500	.556	.507	.464	.426	.392	.363	.336	.313	.292	.273	.255	.240	.225	.212	.200	.189	.179	.170	.161	.153
550	.612	.557	.510	.468	.432	.399	.370	.344	.321	.300	.281	.263	.248	.233	.220	.208	.197	.187	.177	.169
600	.667	.608	.556	.511	.471	.435	.404	.375	.350	.327	.306	.287	.270	.255	.240	.227	.215	.204	.194	.184
650	.723	.659	.603	.554	.510	.472	.437	.407	.379	.354	.332	.311	.293	.276	.260	.246	.233	.221	.210	.199
700	.779	.710	.649	.596	.549	.508	.471	.438	.408	.382	.357	.335	.315	.297	.280	.265	.251	.238	.226	.215
750	.834	.760	.696	.639	.589	.544	.505	.469	.438	.409	.383	.359	.338	.318	.300	.284	.269	.255	.242	.230
800	.890	.811	.742	.681	.628	.581	.538	.501	.467	.436	.408	.383	.360	.340	.320	.303	.287	.272	.258	.245
850	.946	.862	.788	.724	.667	.617	.572	.532	.496	.463	.434	.407	.383	.361	.340	.322	.305	.289	.274	.261
900	1.00	.912	.835	.767	.706	.653	.606	.563	.525	.491	.459	.431	.405	.382	.360	.341	.323	.306	.290	.276

VELOCITY IN FEET PER SECOND.

DIAMETER OF PIPE IN INCHES.

IGPM	21"	22"	23"	24"	25"	26"	27"	28"	29"	30"	31"	32"	33"	34"	35"	36"	37"	38"	39"	40"
950	1.06	.963	.881	.809	.746	.689	.639	.594	.554	.518	.485	.455	.428	.403	.380	.360	.340	.323	.306	.291
1000	1.11	1.01	.927	.852	.785	.726	.673	.626	.583	.545	.511	.479	.450	.424	.400	.379	.358	.340	.323	.307
1100	1.22	1.11	1.02	.937	.863	.798	.740	.688	.642	.600	.562	.527	.496	.467	.441	.416	.394	.374	.355	.337
1200	1.33	1.22	1.11	1.02	.942	.871	.808	.751	.700	.654	.613	.575	.541	.509	.481	.454	.430	.408	.387	.368
1300	1.45	1.32	1.21	1.11	1.02	.943	.875	.813	.758	.709	.664	.623	.586	.552	.521	.492	.466	.442	.419	.399
1400	1.56	1.42	1.30	1.19	1.10	1.02	.942	.876	.817	.763	.715	.671	.631	.594	.561	.530	.502	.476	.452	.429
1500	1.67	1.52	1.39	1.28	1.18	1.09	1.01	.939	.875	.818	.766	.719	.676	.637	.601	.568	.538	.510	.484	.460
1600	1.78	1.62	1.48	1.36	1.26	1.16	1.08	1.00	.933	.872	.817	.767	.721	.679	.641	.606	.573	.544	.516	.491
1700	1.89	1.72	1.58	1.45	1.33	1.23	1.14	1.06	.992	.927	.868	.814	.766	.721	.681	.644	.609	.578	.548	.521
1800	2.00	1.82	1.67	1.53	1.41	1.31	1.21	1.13	1.05	.981	.919	.862	.811	.764	.721	.681	.645	.612	.581	.552
1900	2.11	1.93	1.76	1.62	1.49	1.38	1.28	1.19	1.11	1.04	.970	.910	.856	.806	.761	.719	.681	.646	.613	.583
2000	2.22	2.03	1.85	1.70	1.57	1.45	1.35	1.25	1.17	1.09	1.02	.958	.901	.849	.801	.757	.717	.679	.645	.613
2100	2.34	2.13	1.95	1.79	1.65	1.52	1.41	1.31	1.23	1.14	1.07	1.01	.946	.891	.841	.795	.753	.713	.677	.644
2200	2.45	2.23	2.04	1.87	1.73	1.60	1.48	1.38	1.28	1.20	1.12	1.05	.991	.934	.881	.833	.788	.747	.710	.675
2300	2.56	2.33	2.13	1.96	1.81	1.67	1.55	1.44	1.34	1.25	1.17	1.10	1.04	.976	.921	.871	.824	.781	.742	.705
2400	2.67	2.43	2.23	2.04	1.88	1.74	1.62	1.50	1.40	1.31	1.23	1.15	1.08	1.02	.961	.908	.860	.815	.774	.736
2500	2.78	2.53	2.32	2.13	1.96	1.81	1.68	1.56	1.46	1.36	1.28	1.20	1.12	1.06	1.00	.946	.896	.849	.806	.767
2600	2.89	2.64	2.41	2.21	2.04	1.89	1.75	1.63	1.52	1.42	1.33	1.25	1.17	1.10	1.04	.984	.932	.883	.839	.797
2700	3.00	2.74	2.50	2.30	2.12	1.96	1.82	1.69	1.58	1.47	1.38	1.29	1.22	1.15	1.08	1.02	.968	.917	.871	.828
2800	3.11	2.84	2.60	2.38	2.20	2.03	1.88	1.75	1.63	1.53	1.43	1.34	1.26	1.19	1.12	1.06	1.00	.951	.903	.859

VELOCITY IN FEET PER SECOND.

B-6

DIAMETER OF PIPE IN INCHES.

IGPM	21"	22"	23"	24"	25"	26"	27"	28"	29"	30"	31"	32"	33"	34"	35"	36"	37"	38"	39"	40"
2900	3.23	2.94	2.69	2.47	2.28	2.10	1.95	1.81	1.69	1.58	1.48	1.39	1.31	1.23	1.16	1.10	1.04	.985	.935	.889
3000	3.34	3.04	2.78	2.56	2.35	2.18	2.02	1.88	1.75	1.64	1.53	1.44	1.35	1.27	1.20	1.14	1.08	1.02	.968	.920
3200	3.56	3.24	2.97	2.73	2.51	2.32	2.15	2.00	1.82	1.74	1.63	1.53	1.44	1.36	1.28	1.21	1.15	1.09	1.03	.981
3400	3.78	3.45	3.15	2.90	2.67	2.47	2.29	2.13	1.98	1.85	1.74	1.63	1.53	1.44	1.36	1.29	1.22	1.16	1.10	1.04
3600	4.00	3.65	3.34	3.07	2.83	2.61	2.42	2.25	2.10	1.96	1.84	1.72	1.62	1.53	1.44	1.36	1.29	1.22	1.16	1.10
3800	4.23	3.85	3.52	3.24	2.98	2.76	2.56	2.38	2.22	2.07	1.94	1.82	1.71	1.61	1.52	1.44	1.36	1.29	1.23	1.17
4000	4.45	4.05	3.71	3.41	3.14	2.90	2.69	2.50	2.33	2.18	2.04	1.92	1.80	1.70	1.60	1.51	1.43	1.36	1.29	1.23
4500	5.01	4.56	4.17	3.83	3.53	3.27	3.03	2.82	2.63	2.45	2.30	2.16	2.03	1.91	1.80	1.70	1.61	1.53	1.45	1.38
5000	5.56	5.07	4.64	4.26	3.92	3.63	3.36	3.13	2.92	2.73	2.55	2.40	2.25	2.12	2.00	1.89	1.79	1.70	1.61	1.53
5500	6.12	5.57	5.10	4.68	4.32	3.99	3.70	3.44	3.21	3.00	2.81	2.63	2.48	2.33	2.20	2.08	1.97	1.87	1.77	1.69
6000	6.67	6.08	5.56	5.11	4.71	4.35	4.04	3.75	3.50	3.27	3.06	2.87	2.70	2.55	2.40	2.27	2.15	2.04	1.94	1.84
6500	7.23	6.59	6.03	5.54	5.10	4.72	4.37	4.07	3.79	3.54	3.32	3.11	2.93	2.76	2.60	2.46	2.33	2.21	2.10	1.99
7000	7.79	7.10	6.49	5.96	5.49	5.08	4.71	4.38	4.08	3.82	3.57	3.35	3.15	2.97	2.80	2.65	2.51	2.38	2.26	2.15
7500	8.34	7.60	6.96	6.39	5.89	5.44	5.05	4.69	4.38	4.09	3.83	3.59	3.38	3.18	3.00	2.84	2.69	2.55	2.42	2.30
8000	8.90	8.11	7.42	6.81	6.28	5.81	5.38	5.01	4.67	4.36	4.08	3.83	3.60	3.40	3.20	3.03	2.87	2.72	2.58	2.45
8500	9.46	8.62	7.88	7.24	6.67	6.17	5.72	5.32	4.96	4.63	4.34	4.07	3.83	3.61	3.40	3.22	3.05	2.89	2.74	2.61
9000	10.0	9.12	8.35	7.67	7.06	6.53	6.06	5.63	5.25	4.91	4.59	4.31	4.05	3.82	3.60	3.41	3.23	3.06	2.90	2.76
9500	10.6	9.63	8.81	8.09	7.46	6.89	6.39	5.94	5.54	5.18	4.85	4.55	4.28	4.03	3.80	3.60	3.40	3.23	3.06	2.91
10000	11.1	10.1	9.27	8.52	7.85	7.26	6.73	6.26	5.83	5.45	5.11	4.79	4.50	4.24	4.00	3.79	3.58	3.40	3.23	3.07
10500	11.7	10.6	9.74	8.94	8.24	7.62	7.07	6.57	6.13	5.72	5.36	5.03	4.73	4.46	4.20	3.97	3.76	3.57	3.39	3.22

VELOCITY IN FEET PER SECOND.

DIAMETER OF PIPE IN INCHES.

IGPM	21"	22"	23"	24"	25"	26"	27"	28"	29"	30"	31"	32"	33"	34"	35"	36"	37"	38"	39"	40"
11000	12.2	11.1	10.1	9.37	8.63	7.98	7.40	6.88	6.42	6.00	5.62	5.27	4.96	4.67	4.41	4.16	3.94	3.74	3.55	3.37
11500	12.8	11.7	10.7	9.79	9.03	8.35	7.74	7.20	6.71	6.27	5.87	5.51	5.18	4.88	4.61	4.35	4.12	3.91	3.71	3.53
12000	13.3	12.2	11.1	10.2	9.42	8.71	8.08	7.51	7.00	6.54	6.13	5.75	5.41	5.09	4.81	4.54	4.30	4.08	3.87	3.68
12500	13.9	12.7	11.6	10.6	9.81	9.07	8.41	7.82	7.29	6.81	6.38	5.99	5.63	5.30	5.01	4.73	4.48	4.25	4.03	3.83
13000	14.5	13.2	12.1	11.1	10.2	9.43	8.75	8.13	7.58	7.09	6.64	6.23	5.86	5.52	5.21	4.92	4.66	4.42	4.19	3.99
13500	15.0	13.7	12.5	11.5	10.6	9.80	9.08	8.45	7.88	7.36	6.89	6.47	6.08	5.73	5.41	5.11	4.84	4.59	4.35	4.14
14000	15.6	14.2	13.0	11.9	11.0	10.2	9.42	8.76	8.17	7.63	7.15	6.71	6.31	5.94	5.61	5.30	5.02	4.76	4.52	4.29
14500	16.1	14.7	13.4	12.3	11.4	10.5	9.76	9.07	8.46	7.90	7.40	6.95	6.53	6.15	5.81	5.49	5.20	4.93	4.68	4.45
15000	16.7	15.2	13.9	12.8	11.8	10.9	10.1	9.39	8.75	8.18	7.66	7.19	6.76	6.37	6.01	5.68	5.38	5.10	4.84	4.60
15500	17.2	15.7	14.4	13.2	12.2	11.2	10.4	9.70	9.04	8.45	7.91	7.43	6.98	6.58	6.21	5.87	5.55	5.27	5.00	4.75
16000	17.8	16.2	14.8	13.6	12.6	11.6	10.8	10.0	9.33	8.72	8.17	7.67	7.21	6.79	6.41	6.06	5.73	5.44	5.16	4.91
16500	18.4	16.7	15.3	14.1	13.0	12.0	11.1	10.3	9.63	8.99	8.42	7.90	7.43	7.00	6.61	6.25	5.91	5.61	5.32	5.06
17000	18.9	17.2	15.8	14.5	13.3	12.3	11.4	10.6	9.92	9.27	8.68	8.14	7.66	7.21	6.81	6.44	6.09	5.78	5.48	5.21
17500	19.5	17.7	16.2	14.9	13.7	12.7	11.8	11.0	10.2	9.54	8.93	8.38	7.88	7.43	7.01	6.62	6.27	5.95	5.64	5.37
18000	20.0	18.2	16.7	15.3	14.1	13.1	12.1	11.3	10.5	9.81	9.19	8.62	8.11	7.64	7.21	6.81	6.45	6.12	5.81	5.52
18500	20.6	18.8	17.2	15.8	14.5	13.4	12.4	11.6	10.8	10.1	9.44	8.86	8.33	7.85	7.41	7.00	6.63	6.29	5.97	5.67
19000	21.1	19.3	17.6	16.2	14.9	13.8	12.8	11.9	11.1	10.4	9.70	9.10	8.56	8.06	7.61	7.19	6.81	6.46	6.13	5.83
19500	21.7	19.8	18.1	16.6	15.3	14.2	13.1	12.2	11.4	10.6	9.95	9.34	8.78	8.28	7.81	7.38	6.99	6.62	6.29	5.98
20000	22.2	20.3	18.5	17.0	15.7	14.5	13.5	12.5	11.7	10.9	10.2	9.58	9.01	8.49	8.01	7.57	7.17	6.79	6.45	6.13
21000	23.4	21.3	19.5	17.9	16.5	15.2	14.1	13.1	12.3	11.4	10.7	10.1	9.46	8.91	8.41	7.95	7.53	7.13	6.77	6.44

VELOCITY IN FEET PER SECOND.

B-8

DIAMETER OF PIPE IN INCHES.

IGPM	21"	22"	23"	24"	25"	26"	27"	28"	29"	30"	31"	32"	33"	34"	35"	36"	37"	38"	39"	40"
22000	24.5	22.3	20.4	18.7	17.3	16.0	14.8	13.8	12.8	12.0	11.2	10.5	9.91	9.34	8.81	8.33	7.88	7.47	7.10	6.75
23000	25.6	23.3	21.3	19.6	18.1	16.7	15.5	14.4	13.4	12.5	11.7	11.0	10.4	9.76	9.21	8.71	8.24	7.81	7.42	7.05
24000	26.7	24.3	22.3	20.4	18.8	17.4	16.2	15.0	14.0	13.1	12.3	11.5	10.8	10.2	9.61	9.08	8.60	8.15	7.74	7.36
25000	27.8	25.3	23.2	21.3	19.6	18.1	16.8	15.6	14.6	13.6	12.8	12.0	11.2	10.6	10.0	9.46	8.96	8.49	8.06	7.67
26000	28.9	26.4	24.1	22.1	20.4	18.9	17.5	16.3	15.2	14.2	13.3	12.5	11.7	11.0	10.4	9.84	9.32	8.83	8.39	7.97
27000	30.0	27.4	25.0	23.0	21.2	19.6	18.2	16.9	15.8	14.7	13.8	12.9	12.2	11.5	10.8	10.2	9.68	9.17	8.71	8.28
28000	31.1	28.4	26.0	23.8	22.0	20.3	18.8	17.5	16.3	15.3	14.3	13.4	12.6	11.9	11.2	10.6	10.0	9.51	9.03	8.59
29000	32.3	29.4	26.9	24.7	22.8	21.0	19.5	18.1	16.9	15.8	14.8	13.9	13.1	12.3	11.6	11.0	10.4	9.85	9.35	8.89
30000	33.4	30.4	27.8	25.6	23.5	21.8	20.2	18.8	17.5	16.4	15.3	14.4	13.5	12.7	12.0	11.4	10.8	10.2	9.68	9.20
31000	34.5	31.4	28.7	26.4	24.3	22.5	20.9	19.4	18.1	16.9	15.8	14.9	14.0	13.2	12.4	11.7	11.1	10.5	10.0	9.50
32000	35.6	32.4	29.7	27.3	25.1	23.2	21.5	20.0	18.7	17.4	16.3	15.3	14.4	13.6	12.8	12.1	11.5	10.9	10.3	9.81
33000	36.7	33.4	30.6	28.1	25.9	23.9	22.2	20.6	19.3	18.0	16.8	15.8	14.9	14.0	13.2	12.5	11.8	11.2	10.6	10.1
34000	37.8	34.5	31.5	29.0	26.7	24.7	22.9	21.3	19.8	18.5	17.4	16.3	15.3	14.4	13.6	12.9	12.2	11.6	11.0	10.4
35000	38.9	35.5	32.5	29.8	27.5	25.4	23.6	21.9	20.4	19.1	17.9	16.8	15.8	14.9	14.0	13.2	12.5	11.9	11.3	10.7
36000					28.3	26.1	24.2	22.5	21.0	19.6	18.4	17.2	16.2	15.3	14.4	13.6	12.9	12.2	11.6	11.0
37000					29.0	26.9	24.9	23.2	21.6	20.2	18.9	17.7	16.7	15.7	14.8	14.0	13.3	12.6	11.9	11.3
38000						27.6	25.6	23.8	22.2	20.7	19.4	18.2	17.1	16.1	15.2	14.4	13.6	12.9	12.3	11.7
39000						28.3	26.2	24.4	22.8	21.3	19.9	18.7	17.6	16.6	15.6	14.8	14.0	13.2	12.6	12.0
40000							26.9	25.0	23.3	21.8	20.4	19.2	18.0	17.0	16.0	15.1	14.3	13.6	12.9	12.3
41000							27.6	25.7	23.9	22.3	20.9	19.6	18.5	17.4	16.4	15.5	14.7	13.9	13.2	12.6

VELOCITY IN FEET PER SECOND.

B-9

DIAMETER OF PIPE IN INCHES.

IGPM	21"	22"	23"	24"	25"	26"	27"	28"	29"	30"	31"	32"	33"	34"	35"	36"	37"	38"	39"	40"
42000								26.3	24.5	22.9	21.4	20.1	18.9	17.8	16.8	15.9	15.1	14.3	13.5	12.9
43000								26.9	25.1	23.4	22.0	20.6	19.4	18.2	17.2	16.3	15.4	14.6	13.9	13.2
44000								27.5	25.7	24.0	22.5	21.1	19.8	18.7	17.6	16.7	15.8	14.9	14.2	13.5
45000								28.2	26.3	24.5	23.0	21.6	20.3	19.1	18.0	17.0	16.1	15.3	14.5	13.8
46000									26.8	25.1	23.5	22.0	20.7	19.5	18.4	17.4	16.5	15.6	14.8	14.1
47000									27.4	25.6	24.0	22.5	21.2	19.9	18.8	17.8	16.8	16.0	15.2	14.4
48000									28.0	26.2	24.5	23.0	21.6	20.4	19.2	18.2	17.2	16.3	15.5	14.7
49000										26.7	25.0	23.5	22.1	20.8	19.6	18.5	17.6	16.6	15.8	15.0
50000										27.3	25.5	24.0	22.5	21.2	20.0	18.9	17.9	17.0	16.1	15.3
52000											26.5	24.9	23.4	22.1	20.8	19.7	18.6	17.7	16.8	15.9
54000											27.6	25.9	24.3	22.9	21.6	20.4	19.4	18.3	17.4	16.6
56000											28.6	26.8	25.2	23.8	22.4	21.2	20.1	19.0	18.1	17.2
58000											29.6	27.8	26.1	24.6	23.2	22.0	20.8	19.7	18.7	17.8
60000											30.6	28.7	27.0	25.5	24.0	22.7	21.5	20.4	19.4	18.4
62000												29.7	27.9	26.3	24.8	23.5	22.2	21.1	20.0	19.0
64000												30.7	28.8	27.2	25.6	24.2	22.9	21.7	20.6	19.6
66000												31.6	29.7	28.0	26.4	25.0	23.7	22.4	21.3	20.2
68000												32.6	30.6	28.9	27.2	25.7	24.4	23.1	21.9	20.8
70000												33.5	31.5	29.7	28.0	26.5	25.1	23.8	22.6	21.5
75000													33.8	31.8	30.0	28.4	26.9	25.5	24.2	23.0

B-10

VELOCITY IN FEET PER SECOND.

DIAMETER OF PIPE IN INCHES.

IGPM	21"	22"	23"	24"	25"	26"	27"	28"	29"	30"	31"	32"	33"	34"	35"	36"	37"	38"	39"	40"
80000														34.0	32.0	30.3	28.7	27.2	25.8	24.5
85000														36.1	34.0	32.2	30.5	28.9	27.4	26.1
90000														38.2	36.0	34.1	32.3	30.6	29.0	27.6
95000															38.0	36.0	34.0	32.3	30.6	29.1
100000															40.0	37.9	35.8	34.0	32.3	30.7
110000																41.6	39.4	37.4	35.5	33.7
120000																	43.0	40.8	38.7	36.8
130000																			41.9	39.9
140000																				42.9
150000																				
160000																				
170000																				
180000																				
190000																				
200000																				
210000																				
220000																				
230000																				
240000																				
250000																				

VELOCITY IN FEET PER SECOND.

DIAMETER OF PIPE IN INCHES.

C-4

IGPM	41"	42"	43"	44"	45"	46"	47"	48"	49"	50"	51"	52"	53"	54"	55"	56"	57"	58"	59"	60"
280																				
300																				
320	.0934																			
340	.0992	.0946																		
360	.105	.100	.0955																	
380	.111	.106	.101	.0963																
400	.117	.111	.106	.101	.0969															
420	.123	.117	.111	.106	.102	.0974														
440	.128	.122	.117	.111	.107	.102	.0977													
460	.134	.128	.122	.117	.111	.107	.102	.0979												
480	.140	.133	.127	.122	.116	.111	.107	.102	.098											
500	.146	.139	.133	.127	.121	.116	.111	.106	.102	.0981	.0943									
550	.161	.153	.146	.139	.133	.128	.122	.117	.112	.108	.104	.0998	.0961	.0925						
600	.175	.167	.159	.152	.145	.139	.133	.128	.123	.118	.113	.109	.105	.101	.0973	.0939				
650	.190	.181	.172	.165	.157	.151	.144	.138	.133	.128	.123	.118	.114	.109	.105	.102	.0981	.0948		
700	.204	.195	.186	.177	.170	.162	.155	.149	.143	.137	.132	.127	.122	.118	.114	.110	.106	.102	.0987	.0954
750	.219	.209	.199	.190	.182	.174	.167	.160	.153	.147	.141	.136	.131	.126	.122	.117	.113	.109	.106	.102
800	.233	.222	.212	.203	.194	.185	.178	.170	.163	.157	.151	.145	.140	.135	.130	.125	.121	.117	.113	.109
850	.248	.236	.226	.215	.206	.197	.189	.181	.174	.167	.160	.154	.148	.143	.138	.133	.128	.124	.120	.116
900	.263	.250	.239	.228	.218	.209	.200	.192	.184	.177	.170	.163	.157	.151	.146	.141	.136	.131	.127	.123

C-5

VELOCITY IN FEET PER SECOND.
DIAMETER OF PIPE IN INCHES.

IGPM	41"	42"	43"	44"	45"	46"	47"	48"	49"	50"	51"	52"	53"	54"	55"	56"	57"	58"	59"	60"
950	.277	.264	.252	.241	.230	.220	.211	.202	.194	.186	.179	.172	.166	.160	.154	.149	.143	.139	.134	.129
1000	.292	.278	.265	.253	.242	.232	.222	.213	.204	.196	.189	.181	.175	.168	.162	.156	.151	.146	.141	.136
1100	.321	.306	.292	.279	.266	.255	.244	.234	.225	.216	.207	.200	.192	.185	.178	.172	.166	.160	.155	.150
1200	.350	.334	.318	.304	.291	.278	.267	.256	.245	.235	.226	.218	.210	.202	.195	.188	.181	.175	.169	.164
1300	.379	.362	.345	.329	.315	.301	.289	.277	.266	.255	.245	.236	.227	.219	.211	.203	.196	.190	.183	.177
1400	.409	.389	.371	.355	.339	.325	.311	.298	.286	.275	.264	.254	.244	.236	.227	.219	.211	.204	.197	.191
1500	.438	.417	.398	.380	.363	.348	.333	.319	.306	.294	.283	.272	.262	.252	.243	.235	.226	.219	.211	.204
1600	.467	.445	.425	.405	.388	.371	.355	.341	.327	.314	.302	.290	.279	.269	.259	.250	.242	.233	.225	.218
1700	.496	.473	.451	.431	.412	.394	.378	.362	.347	.334	.321	.308	.297	.286	.276	.266	.257	.248	.240	.232
1800	.525	.501	.478	.456	.436	.417	.400	.383	.368	.353	.340	.327	.314	.303	.292	.282	.272	.262	.254	.245
1900	.554	.528	.504	.481	.460	.440	.422	.405	.388	.373	.358	.345	.332	.320	.308	.297	.287	.277	.268	.259
2000	.584	.556	.531	.507	.485	.464	.444	.426	.409	.392	.377	.363	.349	.336	.324	.313	.302	.292	.282	.273
2100	.613	.584	.557	.532	.509	.487	.466	.447	.429	.412	.396	.381	.367	.353	.341	.329	.317	.306	.296	.286
2200	.642	.612	.584	.557	.533	.510	.489	.468	.449	.432	.415	.399	.384	.370	.357	.344	.332	.321	.310	.300
2300	.671	.640	.610	.583	.557	.533	.511	.490	.470	.451	.434	.417	.402	.387	.373	.360	.347	.335	.324	.313
2400	.700	.667	.637	.608	.581	.556	.533	.511	.490	.471	.453	.435	.419	.404	.389	.375	.362	.350	.338	.327
2500	.730	.695	.663	.634	.606	.580	.555	.532	.511	.491	.472	.454	.437	.421	.405	.391	.377	.365	.352	.341
2600	.759	.723	.690	.659	.630	.603	.577	.554	.531	.510	.490	.472	.454	.437	.422	.407	.393	.379	.366	.354
2700	.788	.751	.716	.684	.654	.626	.600	.575	.551	.530	.509	.490	.472	.454	.438	.422	.408	.394	.381	.368
2800	.817	.779	.743	.710	.678	.649	.622	.596	.572	.549	.528	.508	.489	.471	.454	.438	.423	.408	.395	.382

C-6

VELOCITY IN FEET PER SECOND.

DIAMETER OF PIPE IN INCHES.

IGPM	41"	42"	43"	44"	45"	46"	47"	48"	49"	50"	51"	52"	53"	54"	55"	56"	57"	58"	59"	60"
2900	.846	.807	.769	.735	.703	.672	.644	.617	.592	.569	.547	.526	.506	.488	.470	.454	.438	.423	.409	.395
3000	.876	.834	.796	.760	.727	.696	.666	.639	.613	.589	.566	.544	.524	.505	.487	.469	.453	.437	.423	.409
3200	.934	.890	.849	.811	.775	.742	.711	.681	.654	.628	.604	.581	.559	.538	.519	.501	.483	.467	.451	.436
3400	.992	.946	.902	.862	.824	.788	.755	.724	.694	.667	.641	.617	.594	.572	.551	.532	.513	.496	.479	.463
3600	1.05	1.00	.955	.912	.872	.835	.800	.767	.735	.706	.679	.653	.629	.606	.584	.563	.544	.525	.507	.491
3800	1.11	1.06	1.01	.963	.921	.881	.844	.809	.776	.746	.717	.689	.664	.639	.616	.594	.574	.554	.536	.518
4000	1.17	1.11	1.06	1.01	.969	.927	.888	.852	.817	.785	.754	.726	.699	.673	.649	.626	.604	.583	.564	.545
4500	1.31	1.25	1.19	1.14	1.09	1.04	.999	.958	.919	.883	.849	.816	.786	.757	.730	.704	.679	.656	.634	.613
5000	1.46	1.39	1.33	1.27	1.21	1.16	1.11	1.06	1.02	.981	.943	.907	.873	.841	.811	.782	.755	.729	.705	.681
5500	1.61	1.53	1.46	1.39	1.33	1.28	1.22	1.17	1.12	1.08	1.04	.998	.961	.925	.892	.860	.830	.802	.775	.749
6000	1.75	1.67	1.59	1.52	1.45	1.39	1.33	1.28	1.23	1.18	1.13	1.09	1.05	1.01	.973	.939	.906	.875	.846	.818
6500	1.90	1.81	1.72	1.65	1.57	1.51	1.44	1.38	1.33	1.28	1.23	1.18	1.14	1.09	1.05	1.02	.981	.948	.916	.886
7000	2.04	1.95	1.86	1.77	1.70	1.62	1.55	1.49	1.43	1.37	1.32	1.27	1.22	1.18	1.14	1.10	1.06	1.02	.987	.954
7500	2.19	2.09	1.99	1.90	1.82	1.74	1.67	1.60	1.53	1.47	1.41	1.36	1.31	1.26	1.22	1.17	1.13	1.09	1.06	1.02
8000	2.33	2.22	2.12	2.03	1.94	1.85	1.78	1.70	1.63	1.57	1.51	1.45	1.40	1.35	1.30	1.25	1.21	1.17	1.13	1.09
8500	2.48	2.36	2.26	2.15	2.06	1.97	1.89	1.81	1.74	1.67	1.60	1.54	1.48	1.43	1.38	1.33	1.28	1.24	1.20	1.16
9000	2.63	2.50	2.39	2.28	2.18	2.09	2.00	1.92	1.84	1.77	1.70	1.63	1.57	1.51	1.46	1.41	1.36	1.31	1.27	1.23
9500	2.77	2.64	2.52	2.41	2.30	2.20	2.11	2.02	1.94	1.86	1.79	1.72	1.66	1.60	1.54	1.49	1.43	1.39	1.34	1.29
10000	2.92	2.78	2.65	2.53	2.42	2.32	2.22	2.13	2.04	1.96	1.89	1.81	1.75	1.68	1.62	1.56	1.51	1.46	1.41	1.36
10500	3.06	2.92	2.79	2.66	2.54	2.43	2.33	2.24	2.14	2.06	1.98	1.91	1.83	1.77	1.70	1.64	1.59	1.53	1.48	1.43

VELOCITY IN FEET PER SECOND.

DIAMETER OF PIPE IN INCHES.

IGPM	41"	42"	43"	44"	45"	46"	47"	48"	49"	50"	51"	52"	53"	54"	55"	56"	57"	58"	59"	60"
11000	3.21	3.06	2.92	2.79	2.66	2.55	2.44	2.34	2.25	2.16	2.07	2.00	1.92	1.85	1.78	1.72	1.66	1.60	1.55	1.50
11500	3.36	3.20	3.05	2.91	2.79	2.67	2.55	2.45	2.35	2.26	2.17	2.09	2.01	1.93	1.86	1.80	1.74	1.68	1.62	1.57
12000	3.50	3.34	3.18	3.04	2.91	2.78	2.67	2.56	2.45	2.35	2.26	2.18	2.10	2.02	1.95	1.88	1.81	1.75	1.69	1.64
12500	3.65	3.48	3.32	3.17	3.03	2.90	2.78	2.66	2.55	2.45	2.36	2.27	2.18	2.10	2.03	1.96	1.89	1.82	1.76	1.70
13000	3.79	3.62	3.45	3.29	3.15	3.01	2.89	2.77	2.66	2.55	2.45	2.36	2.27	2.19	2.11	2.03	1.96	1.90	1.83	1.77
13500	3.94	3.75	3.58	3.42	3.27	3.13	3.00	2.87	2.76	2.65	2.55	2.45	2.36	2.27	2.19	2.11	2.04	1.97	1.90	1.84
14000	4.09	3.89	3.71	3.55	3.39	3.25	3.11	2.98	2.86	2.75	2.64	2.54	2.44	2.36	2.27	2.19	2.11	2.04	1.97	1.91
14500	4.23	4.03	3.85	3.67	3.51	3.36	3.22	3.09	2.96	2.85	2.73	2.63	2.53	2.44	2.35	2.27	2.19	2.11	2.04	1.98
15000	4.38	4.17	3.98	3.80	3.63	3.48	3.33	3.19	3.06	2.94	2.83	2.72	2.62	2.52	2.43	2.35	2.26	2.19	2.11	2.04
15500	4.52	4.31	4.11	3.93	3.75	3.59	3.44	3.30	3.17	3.04	2.92	2.81	2.71	2.61	2.51	2.42	2.34	2.26	2.18	2.11
16000	4.67	4.45	4.25	4.05	3.88	3.71	3.55	3.41	3.27	3.14	3.02	2.90	2.79	2.69	2.59	2.50	2.42	2.33	2.25	2.18
16500	4.82	4.59	4.38	4.18	4.00	3.83	3.66	3.51	3.37	3.24	3.11	2.99	2.88	2.78	2.68	2.58	2.49	2.41	2.33	2.25
17000	4.96	4.73	4.51	4.31	4.12	3.94	3.78	3.62	3.47	3.34	3.21	3.08	2.97	2.86	2.76	2.66	2.57	2.48	2.40	2.32
17500	5.11	4.87	4.64	4.43	4.24	4.06	3.89	3.73	3.57	3.43	3.30	3.18	3.06	2.94	2.84	2.74	2.64	2.55	2.47	2.38
18000	5.25	5.01	4.78	4.56	4.36	4.17	4.00	3.83	3.68	3.53	3.40	3.27	3.14	3.03	2.92	2.82	2.72	2.62	2.54	2.45
18500	5.40	5.14	4.91	4.69	4.48	4.29	4.11	3.94	3.78	3.63	3.49	3.36	3.23	3.11	3.00	2.89	2.79	2.70	2.61	2.52
19000	5.54	5.28	5.04	4.81	4.60	4.40	4.22	4.05	3.88	3.73	3.58	3.45	3.32	3.20	3.08	2.97	2.87	2.77	2.68	2.59
19500	5.69	5.42	5.17	4.94	4.72	4.52	4.33	4.15	3.98	3.83	3.68	3.54	3.41	3.28	3.16	3.05	2.94	2.84	2.75	2.66
20000	5.84	5.56	5.31	5.07	4.85	4.64	4.44	4.26	4.09	3.92	3.77	3.63	3.49	3.36	3.24	3.13	3.02	2.92	2.82	2.73
21000	6.13	5.84	5.57	5.32	5.09	4.87	4.66	4.47	4.29	4.12	3.96	3.81	3.67	3.53	3.41	3.29	3.17	3.06	2.96	2.86

C-8

VELOCITY IN FEET PER SECOND.

DIAMETER OF PIPE IN INCHES.

IGPM	41"	42"	43"	44"	45"	46"	47"	48"	49"	50"	51"	52"	53"	54"	55"	56"	57"	58"	59"	60"
22000	6.42	6.12	5.84	5.57	5.33	5.10	4.89	4.68	4.49	4.32	4.15	3.99	3.84	3.70	3.57	3.44	3.32	3.21	3.10	3.00
23000	6.71	6.40	6.10	5.83	5.57	5.33	5.11	4.90	4.70	4.51	4.34	4.17	4.02	3.87	3.73	3.60	3.47	3.35	3.24	3.13
24000	7.00	6.67	6.37	6.08	5.81	5.56	5.33	5.11	4.90	4.71	4.53	4.35	4.19	4.04	3.89	3.75	3.62	3.50	3.38	3.27
25000	7.30	6.95	6.63	6.34	6.06	5.80	5.55	5.32	5.11	4.91	4.72	4.54	4.37	4.21	4.05	3.91	3.77	3.65	3.52	3.41
26000	7.59	7.23	6.90	6.59	6.30	6.03	5.77	5.54	5.31	5.10	4.90	4.72	4.54	4.37	4.22	4.07	3.93	3.79	3.66	3.54
27000	7.88	7.51	7.16	6.84	6.54	6.26	6.00	5.75	5.51	5.30	5.09	4.90	4.72	4.54	4.38	4.22	4.08	3.94	3.81	3.68
28000	8.17	7.79	7.43	7.10	6.78	6.49	6.22	5.96	5.72	5.49	5.28	5.08	4.89	4.71	4.54	4.38	4.23	4.08	3.95	3.82
29000	8.46	8.07	7.69	7.35	7.03	6.72	6.44	6.17	5.92	5.69	5.47	5.26	5.06	4.88	4.70	4.54	4.38	4.23	4.09	3.95
30000	8.76	8.34	7.96	7.60	7.27	6.96	6.66	6.39	6.13	5.89	5.66	5.44	5.24	5.05	4.87	4.69	4.53	4.37	4.23	4.09
31000	9.05	8.62	8.22	7.86	7.51	7.19	6.88	6.60	6.33	6.08	5.85	5.62	5.41	5.22	5.03	4.85	4.68	4.52	4.37	4.22
32000	9.34	8.90	8.49	8.11	7.75	7.42	7.11	6.81	6.54	6.28	6.04	5.81	5.59	5.38	5.19	5.01	4.83	4.67	4.51	4.36
33000	9.63	9.18	8.76	8.36	7.99	7.65	7.33	7.03	6.74	6.48	6.22	5.99	5.76	5.55	5.35	5.16	4.98	4.81	4.65	4.50
34000	9.92	9.46	9.02	8.62	8.24	7.88	7.55	7.24	6.94	6.67	6.41	6.17	5.94	5.72	5.51	5.32	5.13	4.96	4.79	4.63
35000	10.2	9.73	9.29	8.87	8.48	8.11	7.77	7.45	7.15	6.87	6.60	6.35	6.11	5.89	5.68	5.48	5.28	5.10	4.93	4.77
36000	10.5	10.0	9.55	9.12	8.72	8.35	8.00	7.67	7.35	7.06	6.79	6.53	6.29	6.06	5.84	5.63	5.44	5.25	5.07	4.91
37000	10.8	10.3	9.82	9.38	8.96	8.58	8.22	7.88	7.56	7.26	6.98	6.71	6.46	6.22	6.00	5.79	5.59	5.40	5.21	5.04
38000	11.1	10.6	10.1	9.63	9.21	8.81	8.44	8.09	7.76	7.46	7.17	6.89	6.64	6.39	6.16	5.94	5.74	5.54	5.36	5.18
39000	11.4	10.8	10.3	9.88	9.45	9.04	8.66	8.30	7.97	7.65	7.36	7.08	6.81	6.56	6.32	6.10	5.89	5.69	5.50	5.31
40000	11.7	11.1	10.6	10.1	9.69	9.27	8.88	8.52	8.17	7.85	7.54	7.26	6.99	6.73	6.49	6.26	6.04	5.83	5.64	5.45
41000	12.0	11.4	10.9	10.4	9.93	9.51	9.11	8.73	8.37	8.05	7.73	7.44	7.16	6.90	6.65	6.41	6.19	5.98	5.78	5.59

C-9

VELOCITY IN FEET PER SECOND.

DIAMETER OF PIPE IN INCHES.

IGPM	60"	59"	58"	57"	56"	55"	54"	53"	52"	51"	50"	49"	48"	47"	46"	45"	44"	43"	42"	41"
42000	5.72	5.92	6.12	6.34	6.57	6.81	7.07	7.33	7.62	7.92	8.24	8.58	8.94	9.33	9.74	10.2	10.6	11.1	11.7	12.3
43000	5.86	6.06	6.27	6.49	6.73	6.97	7.23	7.51	7.80	8.11	8.44	8.78	9.16	9.55	9.97	10.4	10.9	11.4	12.0	12.5
44000	6.00	6.20	6.42	6.64	6.88	7.14	7.40	7.68	7.98	8.30	8.63	8.99	9.37	9.77	10.2	10.7	11.1	11.7	12.2	12.8
45000	6.13	6.34	6.56	6.79	7.04	7.30	7.57	7.86	8.16	8.49	8.83	9.19	9.58	9.99	10.4	10.9	11.4	11.9	12.5	13.1
46000	6.27	6.48	6.71	6.95	7.20	7.46	7.74	8.03	8.35	8.68	9.03	9.40	9.79	10.2	10.7	11.1	11.7	12.2	12.8	13.4
47000	6.40	6.62	6.85	7.10	7.35	7.62	7.91	8.21	8.53	8.87	9.22	9.60	10.0	10.4	10.9	11.4	11.9	12.5	13.1	13.7
48000	6.54	6.76	7.00	7.25	7.51	7.78	8.08	8.38	8.71	9.05	9.42	9.80	10.2	10.7	11.1	11.6	12.2	12.7	13.3	14.0
49000	6.68	6.91	7.15	7.40	7.67	7.95	8.24	8.56	8.89	9.24	9.62	10.0	10.4	10.9	11.4	11.9	12.4	13.0	13.6	14.3
50000	6.81	7.05	7.29	7.55	7.82	8.11	8.41	8.73	9.07	9.43	9.81	10.2	10.6	11.1	11.6	12.1	12.7	13.3	13.9	14.6
52000	7.09	7.33	7.58	7.85	8.13	8.43	8.75	9.08	9.43	9.81	10.2	10.6	11.1	11.5	12.1	12.6	13.2	13.8	14.5	15.2
54000	7.36	7.61	7.87	8.15	8.45	8.76	9.08	9.43	9.80	10.2	10.6	11.0	11.5	12.0	12.5	13.1	13.7	14.3	15.0	15.8
56000	7.63	7.89	8.17	8.46	8.76	9.08	9.42	9.78	10.2	10.6	11.0	11.4	11.9	12.4	13.0	13.6	14.2	14.9	15.6	16.3
58000	7.90	8.17	8.46	8.76	9.07	9.41	9.76	10.1	10.5	10.9	11.4	11.8	12.3	12.9	13.4	14.1	14.7	15.4	16.1	16.9
60000	8.18	8.46	8.75	9.06	9.39	9.73	10.1	10.5	10.9	11.3	11.8	12.3	12.8	13.3	13.9	14.5	15.2	15.9	16.7	17.5
62000	8.45	8.74	9.04	9.36	9.70	10.1	10.4	10.8	11.2	11.7	12.2	12.7	13.2	13.8	14.4	15.0	15.7	16.4	17.2	18.1
64000	8.72	9.02	9.33	9.66	10.0	10.4	10.8	11.2	11.6	12.1	12.6	13.1	13.6	14.2	14.8	15.5	16.2	17.0	17.8	18.7
66000	8.99	9.03	9.62	9.97	10.3	10.7	11.1	11.5	12.0	12.4	13.0	13.5	14.1	14.7	15.3	16.0	16.7	17.5	18.4	19.3
68000	9.27	9.58	9.92	10.3	10.6	11.0	11.4	11.9	12.3	12.8	13.3	13.9	14.5	15.1	15.8	16.5	17.2	18.0	18.9	19.8
70000	9.54	9.87	10.2	10.6	11.0	11.4	11.8	12.2	12.7	13.2	13.7	14.3	14.9	15.5	16.2	17.0	17.7	18.6	19.5	20.4
75000	10.2	10.6	10.9	11.3	11.7	12.2	12.6	13.1	13.6	14.1	14.7	15.3	16.0	16.7	17.4	18.2	19.0	19.9	20.9	21.9

VELOCITY IN FEET PER SECOND.

DIAMETER OF PIPE IN INCHES.

IGPM	41"	42"	43"	44"	45"	46"	47"	48"	49"	50"	51"	52"	53"	54"	55"	56"	57"	58"	59"	60"
80000	23.3	22.2	21.2	20.3	19.4	18.5	17.8	17.0	16.3	15.7	15.1	14.5	14.0	13.5	13.0	12.5	12.1	11.7	11.3	10.9
85000	24.8	23.6	22.6	21.5	20.6	19.7	18.9	18.1	17.4	16.7	16.0	15.4	14.8	14.3	13.8	13.3	12.8	12.4	12.0	11.6
90000	26.3	25.0	23.9	22.8	21.8	20.9	20.0	19.2	18.4	17.7	17.0	16.3	15.7	15.1	14.6	14.1	13.6	13.1	12.7	12.3
95000	27.7	26.4	25.2	24.1	23.0	22.0	21.1	20.2	19.4	18.6	17.9	17.2	16.6	16.0	15.4	14.9	14.3	13.9	13.4	12.9
100000	29.2	27.8	26.5	25.3	24.2	23.2	22.2	21.3	20.4	19.6	18.9	18.1	17.5	16.8	16.2	15.6	15.1	14.6	14.1	13.6
110000	32.1	30.6	29.2	27.9	26.6	25.5	24.4	23.4	22.5	21.6	20.7	20.0	19.2	18.5	17.8	17.2	16.6	16.0	15.5	15.0
120000	35.0	33.4	31.8	30.4	29.1	27.8	26.7	25.6	24.5	23.5	22.6	21.8	21.0	20.2	19.5	18.8	18.1	17.5	16.9	16.4
130000	37.9	36.2	34.5	32.9	31.5	30.1	28.9	27.7	26.6	25.5	24.5	23.6	22.7	21.9	21.1	20.3	19.6	19.0	18.3	17.7
140000	40.9	38.9	37.1	35.5	33.9	32.5	31.1	29.8	28.6	27.5	26.4	25.4	24.4	23.6	22.7	21.9	21.1	20.4	19.7	19.1
150000	43.8	41.7	39.8	38.0	36.3	34.8	33.3	31.9	30.6	29.4	28.3	27.2	26.2	25.2	24.3	23.5	22.6	21.9	21.1	20.4
160000			42.5	40.5	38.8	37.1	35.5	34.1	32.7	31.4	30.2	29.0	27.9	26.9	25.9	25.0	24.2	23.3	22.5	21.8
170000			45.1	43.1	41.2	39.4	37.8	36.2	34.7	33.4	32.1	30.8	29.7	28.6	27.6	26.6	25.7	24.8	24.0	23.2
180000				45.6	43.6	41.7	40.0	38.2	36.8	35.3	34.0	32.7	31.4	30.3	29.2	28.2	27.2	26.2	25.4	24.5
190000					46.0	44.0	42.2	40.5	38.8	37.3	35.8	34.5	33.2	32.0	30.8	29.7	28.7	27.7	26.8	25.9
200000						46.4	44.4	42.6	40.9	39.2	37.7	36.3	34.9	33.6	32.4	31.3	30.2	29.2	28.2	27.3
210000										41.2	39.6	38.1	36.7	35.3	34.1	32.9	31.7	30.6	29.6	28.6
220000											41.5	39.9	38.4	37.0	35.7	34.4	33.2	32.1	31.0	30.0
230000												41.7	40.2	38.7	37.3	36.0	34.7	33.5	32.4	31.3
240000													41.9	40.4	38.9	37.5	36.2	35.0	33.8	32.7
250000														42.1	40.5	39.1	37.7	36.5	35.2	34.1

VELOCITY IN FEET PER ·SECOND.

DIAMETER OF PIPE IN INCHES.

D-4

IGPM	61"	62"	63"	64"	65"	66"	67"	68"	69"	70"	71"	72"
700	.0923											
750	.0989	.0957										
800	.105	.102	.0989	.0958								
850	.112	.108	.105	.102	.0987	.0957						
900	.119	.115	.111	.108	.104	.101	.0984	.0955				

VELOCITY IN FEET PER SECOND.

DIAMETER OF PIPE IN INCHES.

D-5

IGPM	61"	62"	63"	64"	65"	66"	67"	68"	69"	70"	71"	72"
950	.125	.121	.117	.114	.110	.107	.104	.101	.0979	.0951		
1000	.132	.128	.124	.120	.116	.113	.109	.106	.103	.100	.0973	.0946
1100	.145	.140	.136	.132	.128	.124	.120	.117	.113	.110	.107	.104
1200	.158	.153	.148	.144	.139	.135	.131	.127	.124	.120	.117	.114
1300	.171	.166	.161	.156	.151	.146	.142	.138	.134	.130	.127	.123
1400	.185	.179	.173	.168	.163	.158	.153	.149	.144	.140	.136	.132
1500	.198	.191	.185	.180	.174	.169	.164	.159	.155	.150	.146	.142
1600	.211	.204	.198	.192	.186	.180	.175	.170	.165	.160	.156	.151
1700	.224	.217	.210	.204	.197	.191	.186	.180	.175	.170	.165	.161
1800	.237	.230	.222	.216	.209	.203	.197	.191	.185	.180	.175	.170
1900	.250	.242	.235	.228	.221	.214	.208	.202	.196	.190	.185	.180
2000	.264	.255	.247	.240	.232	.225	.219	.212	.206	.200	.195	.189
2100	.277	.268	.260	.252	.244	.237	.229	.223	.216	.210	.204	.199
2200	.290	.281	.272	.263	.255	.248	.240	.233	.227	.220	.214	.208
2300	.303	.294	.284	.275	.267	.259	.251	.244	.237	.230	.224	.218
2400	.316	.306	.297	.287	.279	.270	.262	.255	.247	.240	.234	.227
2500	.330	.319	.309	.299	.290	.282	.273	.265	.258	.250	.243	.237
2600	.343	.332	.321	.311	.302	.293	.284	.276	.268	.260	.253	.246
2700	.356	.345	.334	.323	.313	.304	.295	.286	.278	.270	.263	.256
2800	.369	.357	.346	.335	.325	.315	.306	.297	.289	.280	.272	.265

VELOCITY IN FEET PER SECOND.

D-6

DIAMETER OF PIPE IN INCHES.

IGPM	61"	62"	63"	64"	65"	66"	67"	68"	69"	70"	71"	72"
2900	.382	.370	.358	.347	.337	.327	.317	.308	.299	.290	.282	.274
3000	.396	.383	.371	.359	.348	.338	.328	.318	.309	.300	.292	.284
3200	.422	.408	.396	.383	.372	.360	.350	.339	.330	.320	.311	.303
3400	.448	.434	.420	.407	.395	.383	.372	.361	.350	.340	.331	.322
3600	.475	.459	.445	.431	.418	.405	.393	.382	.371	.360	.350	.341
3800	.501	.485	.470	.455	.441	.428	.415	.403	.392	.380	.370	.360
4000	.527	.510	.494	.479	.464	.450	.437	.424	.412	.400	.389	.379
4500	.593	.574	.556	.539	.522	.507	.492	.477	.464	.451	.438	.426
5000	.659	.638	.618	.599	.581	.563	.546	.530	.515	.501	.487	.473
5500	.725	.702	.680	.659	.639	.619	.601	.583	.567	.551	.535	.520
6000	.791	.766	.742	.719	.697	.676	.656	.637	.618	.601	.584	.568
6500	.857	.830	.803	.779	.755	.732	.710	.690	.670	.651	.633	.615
7000	.923	.893	.865	.838	.813	.788	.765	.743	.721	.701	.681	.662
7500	.989	.957	.927	.898	.871	.845	.820	.796	.773	.751	.730	.710
8000	1.05	1.02	.989	.958	.929	.901	.874	.849	.824	.801	.779	.757
8500	1.12	1.08	1.05	1.02	.987	.957	.929	.902	.876	.851	.827	.804
9000	1.19	1.16	1.11	1.08	1.04	1.01	.984	.955	.927	.901	.876	.852
9500	1.25	1.21	1.17	1.14	1.10	1.07	1.04	1.01	.979	.951	.925	.899
10000	1.32	1.28	1.24	1.20	1.16	1.13	1.09	1.06	1.03	1.00	.973	.946
10500	1.38	1.34	1.30	1.26	1.22	1.18	1.15	1.11	1.08	1.05	1.02	.994

VELOCITY IN FEET PER SECOND.

DIAMETER OF PIPE IN INCHES.

IGPM	61"	62"	63"	64"	65"	66"	67"	68"	69"	70"	71"	72"
11000	1.45	1.40	1.36	1.32	1.28	1.24	1.20	1.17	1.13	1.10	1.07	1.04
11500	1.52	1.47	1.42	1.38	1.34	1.30	1.26	1.22	1.18	1.15	1.12	1.09
12000	1.58	1.53	1.48	1.44	1.39	1.35	1.31	1.27	1.24	1.20	1.17	1.14
12500	1.65	1.60	1.55	1.50	1.45	1.41	1.37	1.33	1.29	1.25	1.22	1.18
13000	1.71	1.66	1.61	1.56	1.51	1.46	1.42	1.38	1.34	1.30	1.27	1.23
13500	1.78	1.72	1.67	1.62	1.57	1.52	1.48	1.43	1.39	1.35	1.31	1.28
14000	1.85	1.79	1.73	1.68	1.63	1.58	1.53	1.49	1.44	1.40	1.36	1.32
14500	1.91	1.85	1.79	1.74	1.68	1.63	1.58	1.54	1.49	1.45	1.41	1.37
15000	1.98	1.91	1.85	1.80	1.74	1.69	1.64	1.59	1.55	1.50	1.46	1.42
15500	2.04	1.98	1.92	1.86	1.80	1.75	1.69	1.64	1.60	1.55	1.51	1.47
16000	2.11	2.04	1.98	1.92	1.86	1.80	1.75	1.70	1.65	1.60	1.56	1.51
16500	2.18	2.11	2.04	1.98	1.92	1.86	1.80	1.75	1.70	1.65	1.61	1.56
17000	2.24	2.17	2.10	2.04	1.97	1.91	1.86	1.80	1.75	1.70	1.65	1.61
17500	2.31	2.23	2.16	2.10	2.03	1.97	1.91	1.86	1.80	1.75	1.70	1.66
18000	2.37	2.30	2.22	2.16	2.09	2.03	1.97	1.91	1.85	1.80	1.75	1.70
18500	2.44	2.36	2.29	2.22	2.15	2.08	2.02	1.96	1.91	1.85	1.80	1.75
19000	2.50	2.42	2.35	2.28	2.21	2.14	2.08	2.02	1.96	1.90	1.85	1.80
19500	2.57	2.49	2.41	2.34	2.26	2.20	2.13	2.07	2.01	1.95	1.90	1.85
20000	2.64	2.55	2.47	2.40	2.32	2.25	2.19	2.12	2.06	2.00	1.95	1.89
21000	2.77	2.68	2.60	2.52	2.44	2.37	2.29	2.23	2.16	2.10	2.04	1.99

D-8

VELOCITY IN FEET PER SECOND.

DIAMETER OF PIPE IN INCHES.

IGPM	61"	62"	63"	64"	65"	66"	67"	68"	69"	70"	71"	72"
22000	2.90	2.81	2.72	2.63	2.55	2.48	2.40	2.33	2.27	2.20	2.14	2.08
23000	3.03	2.94	2.84	2.75	2.67	2.59	2.51	2.44	2.37	2.30	2.24	2.18
24000	3.16	3.06	2.97	2.87	2.79	2.70	2.62	2.55	2.47	2.40	2.34	2.27
25000	3.30	3.19	3.09	2.99	2.90	2.82	2.73	2.65	2.58	2.50	2.43	2.37
26000	3.43	3.32	3.21	3.11	3.02	2.93	2.84	2.76	2.68	2.60	2.53	2.46
27000	3.56	3.45	3.34	3.23	3.13	3.04	2.95	2.86	2.78	2.70	2.63	2.56
28000	3.69	3.57	3.46	3.35	3.25	3.15	3.06	2.97	2.88	2.80	2.72	2.65
29000	3.82	3.70	3.58	3.47	3.37	3.27	3.17	3.08	2.99	2.90	2.82	2.74
30000	3.96	3.83	3.71	3.59	3.48	3.38	3.28	3.18	3.09	3.00	2.92	2.84
31000	4.09	3.96	3.83	3.71	3.60	3.49	3.39	3.29	3.19	3.10	3.02	2.93
32000	4.22	4.08	3.96	3.83	3.72	3.60	3.50	3.39	3.30	3.20	3.11	3.03
33000	4.35	4.21	4.08	3.95	3.83	3.72	3.61	3.50	3.40	3.30	3.21	3.12
34000	4.48	4.34	4.20	4.07	3.95	3.83	3.72	3.61	3.50	3.40	3.31	3.22
35000	4.61	4.47	4.33	4.19	4.06	3.94	3.82	3.71	3.61	3.50	3.41	3.31
36000	4.75	4.59	4.45	4.31	4.18	4.05	3.93	3.82	3.71	3.60	3.50	3.41
37000	4.88	4.72	4.57	4.43	4.30	4.17	4.04	3.92	3.81	3.70	3.60	3.50
38000	5.01	4.85	4.70	4.55	4.41	4.28	4.15	4.03	3.92	3.80	3.70	3.60
39000	5.14	4.98	4.82	4.67	4.53	4.39	4.26	4.14	4.02	3.90	3.80	3.69
40000	5.27	5.10	4.94	4.79	4.64	4.50	4.37	4.24	4.12	4.00	3.89	3.79
41000	5.41	5.23	5.07	4.91	4.76	4.62	4.48	4.35	4.22	4.10	3.99	3.88

VELOCITY IN FEET PER SECOND.

D-9

IGPM	61"	62"	63"	64"	65"	66"	67"	68"	69"	70"	71"	72"
									DIAMETER OF PIPE IN INCHES.			
42000	5.54	5.36	5.19	5.03	4.88	4.73	4.59	4.46	4.33	4.21	4.09	3.97
43000	5.67	5.49	5.31	5.15	4.99	4.84	4.70	4.56	4.43	4.31	4.18	4.07
44000	5.80	5.62	5.44	5.27	5.11	4.96	4.81	4.67	4.53	4.41	4.28	4.16
45000	5.93	5.74	5.56	5.39	5.22	5.07	4.92	4.77	4.64	4.51	4.38	4.26
46000	6.06	5.87	5.69	5.51	5.34	5.18	5.03	4.88	4.74	4.61	4.48	4.35
47000	6.20	6.00	5.81	5.63	5.46	5.29	5.14	4.99	4.84	4.71	4.57	4.45
48000	6.33	6.13	5.93	5.75	5.57	5.41	5.25	5.09	4.95	4.81	4.67	4.54
49000	6.46	6.25	6.06	5.87	5.69	5.52	5.35	5.20	5.05	4.91	4.77	4.64
50000	6.59	6.38	6.18	5.99	5.81	5.63	5.46	5.30	5.15	5.01	4.87	4.73
52000	6.86	6.64	6.43	6.23	6.04	5.86	5.68	5.52	5.36	5.21	5.06	4.92
54000	7.12	6.89	6.67	6.47	6.27	6.08	5.90	5.73	5.56	5.41	5.26	5.11
56000	7.38	7.15	6.92	6.71	6.50	6.31	6.12	5.94	5.77	5.61	5.45	5.30
58000	7.65	7.40	7.17	6.95	6.73	6.53	6.34	6.15	5.98	5.81	5.64	5.49
60000	7.91	7.66	7.42	7.19	6.97	6.76	6.56	6.37	6.18	6.01	5.84	5.68
62000	8.17	7.91	7.66	7.43	7.20	6.98	6.78	6.58	6.39	6.21	6.03	5.87
64000	8.44	8.17	7.91	7.67	7.43	7.21	6.99	6.79	6.59	6.41	6.23	6.06
66000	8.70	8.42	8.16	7.90	7.66	7.43	7.21	7.00	6.80	6.61	6.42	6.25
68000	8.97	8.68	8.40	8.14	7.90	7.66	7.43	7.21	7.01	6.81	6.62	6.44
70000	9.23	8.93	8.65	8.38	8.13	7.88	7.65	7.43	7.21	7.01	6.81	6.62
75000	9.89	9.57	9.27	8.98	8.71	8.45	8.20	7.96	7.73	7.51	7.30	7.10

D-10

VELOCITY IN FEET PER SECOND.

DIAMETER OF PIPE IN INCHES.

IGPM	61"	62"	63"	64"	65"	66"	67"	68"	69"	70"	71"	72"
80000	10.5	10.2	9.89	9.58	9.29	9.01	8.74	8.49	8.24	8.01	7.79	7.57
85000	11.2	10.8	10.5	10.2	9.87	9.57	9.29	9.02	8.76	8.51	8.27	8.04
90000	11.9	11.5	11.1	10.8	10.4	10.1	9.84	9.55	9.27	9.01	8.76	8.52
95000	12.5	12.1	11.7	11.4	11.0	10.7	10.4	10.1	9.79	9.51	9.25	8.99
100000	13.2	12.8	12.4	12.0	11.6	11.3	10.9	10.6	10.3	10.0	9.73	9.46
110000	14.5	14.0	13.6	13.2	12.8	12.4	12.0	11.7	11.3	11.0	10.7	10.4
120000	15.8	15.3	14.8	14.4	13.9	13.5	13.1	12.7	12.4	12.0	11.7	11.4
130000	17.1	16.6	16.1	15.6	15.1	14.6	14.2	13.8	13.4	13.0	12.7	12.3
140000	18.5	17.9	17.3	16.8	16.3	15.8	15.3	14.9	14.4	14.0	13.6	13.2
150000	19.8	19.1	18.5	18.0	17.4	16.9	16.4	15.9	15.5	15.0	14.6	14.2
160000	21.1	20.4	19.8	19.2	18.6	18.0	17.5	17.0	16.5	16.0	15.6	15.1
170000	22.4	21.7	21.0	20.4	19.7	19.1	18.6	18.0	17.5	17.0	16.5	16.1
180000	23.7	23.0	22.2	21.6	20.9	20.3	19.7	19.1	18.5	18.0	17.5	17.0
190000	25.0	24.2	23.5	22.8	22.1	21.4	20.8	20.2	19.6	19.0	18.5	18.0
200000	26.4	25.5	24.7	24.0	23.2	22.5	21.9	21.2	20.6	20.0	19.5	18.9
210000	27.7	26.8	26.0	25.2	24.4	23.7	22.9	22.3	21.6	21.0	20.4	19.9
220000	29.0	28.1	27.2	26.3	25.5	24.8	24.0	23.3	22.7	22.0	21.4	20.8
230000	30.3	29.4	28.4	27.5	26.7	25.9	25.1	24.4	23.7	23.0	22.4	21.8
240000	31.6	30.6	29.7	28.7	27.9	27.0	26.2	25.5	24.7	24.0	23.4	22.7
250000	33.0	31.9	30.9	29.9	29.0	28.2	27.3	26.5	25.8	25.0	24.3	23.7

Index